The Link

A Homœopathic Approach to
Healing using the Bowel Nosodes

Doris Beauchamp

First published in Great Britain in 2007 by
Schoenfeld Publishing
3 Craigen Avenue,
Croydon, Surrey
CR0 7JP, UK

DBeauch301@aol.com

Printed and bound in Great Britain by
Antony Rowe Ltd, Chippenham, Wiltshire

British Library Cataloguing in Publication Data
A CIP catalogue record for this book is available from the British Library

ISBN 978-0-9555518-0-2

From 'The Road Not Taken'

By Robert Frost 1875 -1963

Two roads diverged in a wood and I …….
I took the one less travelled by,
And that has made all the difference.

Acknowledgment

I would like to thank everyone who asked questions to which I had to find the answers.

It turned into a quest to link the
Flower of Life with six topics:
the Bowel Nosodes
Iridology,
the Etheric or Energy Bodies,
the Chakras,
the Sarcodes
and the Tissue Salts.

Contents

Preface

This book was 'created' over the past seven years through researching and gathering as much information as I could find on the various topics included in this book, and trying to incorporate the Bowel Nosodes more and more into my practice. The Bowel Nosodes are potentised gut bacteria relating to Bach's theory of intestinal toxaemia. By designing a 'table' of the Bowel Nosodes in relation to the Chakras and Sarcodes I found that I could easily refer back to the Bowel Nosodes at a quick glance, which helped me to improve my understanding of these Nosodes and their relationship to the Polychrests (referring to remedies of many uses), but also to some of the smaller remedies.

The relationship of associated remedies is important here; for example, when seeing a 'typical' Calcarea Carbonica or Sulphur type person you could consider Morgan Pure or Morgan Bach as the Bowel Nosodes (both belonging to the Base Chakra) that would be most beneficial to these patients. Similarly, for the Third Eye at the opposite end of the scale the Bowel Nosode Dysentery-co would profit those in need of Argentum Nitricum or Arsenicum Album, as these two complement Dys-co.

As a diagnostic tool additional to Homœopathy, I studied Iridology allowing me to discover that the Bowel flora (i.e. the bacteria in the gut, as seen in the iris in the area of the intestines) has 'a lot to answer for' when it comes to 'dis-ease' in the body, confirming my desire to start the treatment at the very root of the problem. Although you cannot see the **bacteria** itself, in the same way that you cannot diagnose kidney or gallbladder stones, yet the <u>problems</u> relating to 'bad' or disease-causing bacteria can be seen in the iris.

The gut can point to anxiety in the patient through tightness of the Autonomic Nerve Wreath (called the ANW – a ring about one third of the way out from the pupil). Similarly, the ANW can indicate bloating, which the patient will confirm when asked, or may be of a different colour with breaks in the fibres, or a different fibre structure to the rest of this iris. This wreath is seldom smooth and even all the way around; it can be quite irregular, sometimes even jagged, covering almost half of the iris. The area close to the pupil portrays the stomach, followed by the intestines small and large, being a major landmark in the iris where the first clues of how well or poor the patient's health is may be found.

Having created an entire programme (more about this later) to clear out the bad gut bacteria might not seem like the very 'classical' approach that we are supposed to aim for when looking for the 'mental/emotional' picture. Nonetheless, considering that our intestines – small and large – may be regarded as our 'second brain', we could accept it as being on the right track. Often we talk about a 'gut-feeling' we have, before we analyse a problem mentally in order to figure out the answers. This usually leads to overriding our 'instinct' and these 'gut-feeling', which might mean we make the wrong choice, as our 'unhealthy' dis-ease causing bacteria lead us to make 'impulsive' decisions instead of level-headed thinking. A healthy bowel flora will help us to think clearly, be in command of our destiny and not be 'fearful' to move on, as it is 'fear' and constant 'worries', which lead to inertia that stop us in our tracks.

For example: when prescribing remedies for one of my patients, a relative of mine, she could not understand why I had noted on her remedy bags that the remedies were to 'improve the bowel-flora' when in fact she had the pains in her head – forty years of migraines! Yet, with each month going by, taking the remedies as instructed, she reported having these migraine attacks less often than the month before, until after a year or so they occurred maybe once a month and finally not at all. Furthermore, up to this day (five years later) no re-occurring migraines are taking place. At the beginning of her treatment these had occurred four times a week, requiring very costly and strong medication! Now in her early 70s and no longer suffering from these debilitating headaches she regularly attends the gym to exercise, has lost weight and looks 10 years younger. She has acquired a new lease of life; the 'fear' alone of persistently getting headaches did not allow her to try something new. **Fear** can spoil the enjoyment of life as much as the painful headache itself.

Another very good reason to clear out the 'unwanted' bacteria – the disease causing bowel flora – is its possible contribution to causing bowel cancer, which according to a recent television report (Summer 2005) making the headlines in the news kills 40 people each day in the UK, making it the second biggest cancer killer after lung cancer (with cancer itself being second only to heart disease in terms of most deaths per year in the UK). The symptoms of bowel cancer do not occur suddenly; there is usually a long history of altered bowel habits, either in the form of increased constipation or diarrhoea or an alternation of these. Often it is only when bleeding on a regular basis is taking place that medical advice is sought. Cancer of the small intestine is extremely rare. The colon, however, which houses the 'good' as well as the 'bad' bacteria, is a different story. Consequently it is worthwhile looking at the symptoms of the patients, especially when it comes to the daily routine of emptying the bowels, as well as all the other complaints, and match these with a Bowel Nosode and other miasmatic remedies.

The word 'Miasma' stems from the Greek for 'pollution' or 'taint', which can be acquired through an acute disease, for example Glandular Fever and then having 'never been well since' (shortened to NBWS), or a sexually transmitted disease or vaccination, but also environmental toxins can 'pollute' the body and weaken the immune system. A Miasm (as it is called in homœopathic terminology) can be an inherited predisposition to certain conditions like a cancer or diabetes, passed on in the DNA, now very much recognised by the medical profession as well. The understanding of our DNA was not always the case and certainly not in the days of Hahnemann, the founder of Homœopathy, 250 years ago in Germany. Indeed he was very much 'ahead of his time' so to speak by recognising and labelling these as **Psora**, **Sycosis** and **Syphilis**. This was before a microscopic examination of bacteria was even dreamed of. These modern tools now provide in great details of how these behave in the laboratory on a Petri dish under certain conditions. Dr Edward Bach discoverer of the Bowel Nosodes 150 years later had the advantage of being able to observe them under the microscope, being a bacteriologist. He found some bacteria took as long as 72 hours to produce visual changes, which means that a patient getting sick three days after eating something which caused changes in the bacteria of the gut will not see the connections to the food consumed. We all have to be truly grateful to Hahnemann, his genius and great intuition giving us this 'gentle art of healing', as well as Bach for his research into the bowel flora!

Relating the Bowel Nosodes to the chakras as well as incorporating the **'Sarcodes'**, which are preparations from healthy tissue or secretions, such as hormones, is one of the special foci of this book. The chakras do not have the density of the physical body; they are part of our energy body and could be described as the **LINK** between the two. These 'wheels of energy', as the translation of the word chakra means, act on the stimulation of the nervous system using the hormones as their 'chemical messengers'. If the glands are healthy and work well the messages are related accordingly and all is well. However, these gland are often much abused by our modern lifestyle, for example running on a high **adrenal output**, everything is extremely hectic and in order to be able to keep going people drink lots of strong coffee, leading to exhaustion of the adrenal glands. An additional burden to the body can be an unhealthy diet and snacking all the time. The best example is too much sugar, by constantly consuming chocolate bars to supply a quick boost of energy to the body, therefore stretching the pancreas to its limits and leading to diabetes in the long run, now seen more often in children than ever before (incidentally, easily detected in the iris long before it is possible to be diagnosed). With Sarcodes we can calm the nerves, put a stop to the sweet craving and help children to grow up into healthy and responsible adults, balance the calcium, which will be depleted by the 'wrong diet' while they are growing etc.; whatever is needed uppermost at the time.

Finally, I have included the **Tissue Salts** in this book, looking at the astrological sign of the person to help provide answers by almost predicting what might be lacking according to their 'sun sign'. Looking at the opposite sign is equally important, as will be explained in the relevant chapter. By supplying to the body that which is 'lacking', like cracks appearing in a building or the roof leaking, we can help to restore the body to full vitality and rekindle a 'joy of life', using the tissue salts as support remedies 'as and when' needed.

Although the majority of my research has been finalised for this edition, at the same time I feel there is more I could add to it all the time.

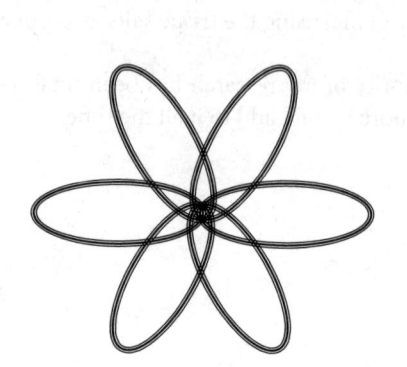

Chapter ONE — Journey to the Bowel Nosodes

The First Step: Sparking an Interest

My first exposure to the Bowel Nosodes was during a lecture on the subject when I was studying homœopathy. Much to my disappointment the presentation was not very inspiring. The subject is simply far too extensive to be explained in just one lecture and thus no blame to the lecturer that the whole thing was unsatisfactory.

I could identify with the Miasm theory and loved the idea of treating the 'family history' and 'letting go' of miasmatic tendencies. The Bowel Nosodes, however, remained a mystery, yet at the same time fascinated me! That the Bowel Nosodes, when traced via the chakras, can indeed be closely related to the Miasms was the LINK I needed to start the journey, as will be explained later.

Growing up as a child in Germany I loved to listen to many enchanting fairy tales. The Miasms to me seem like a 'spell from the past', where at the christening of Sleeping Beauty a nasty fairy godmother spoils the otherwise wonderful gifts bestowed upon her by the rest of the fairies. (I do not see it as a curse, just a 'spell' to make life a little more challenging. Like a baby coming into the world with a sterile gut being introduced to all sorts of bacteria, toxins etc. is part of the challenge called 'survival'.)

The Nosodes can help lessen the burden from the past. That these miasmatic remedies worked like magic very quickly became clear to me during my first year of attending college when I changed my homœopath of many years. I had been treated very classically for about 9 years and had been very patient, waiting for the desired quick recovery! However, thinking that 'good things take time' I certainly did not complain and was grateful for the help I received via the little globules. It meant at the time that I did not have to have an operation, which would have been very much routine in the doctor's eyes; 'nothing to worry about', as they often say. In fact they could not understand why I preferred to suffer pain, in my case terrible gall-bladder colic, rather than have the 'offending' organ removed.

Even my homœopath at one time had said that if the gall-bladder was always inflamed it might be better to have it taken out as it could turn cancerous. Well, that was not why I chose Homœopathy: I wanted to avoid having to go under the knife; I wanted those little sugar pills to work their MAGIC! And that is exactly what they have done for me!

Admittedly, it was not an overnight success and patience was needed. Yet, with the aid of the **Bowel Nosodes** things took off in a big way. I cannot thank my Homœopath Jan Walker, in Wimbledon, enough for what she did for me and what she taught me and others when attending her tutorials. Not only did she remove layer after layer of 'family stuff', but also my own 'acquired miasms', almost in record time.

I had always suffered from constipation, ever since childhood and this started most likely after my first course of antibiotics during an episode of scarlet fever, which caused the base chakra to be blocked and resulted in a lack of movement in this 'energy wheel'. Adding further to the blockage in the base chakra was a very emotional and physical trauma of having my tonsils removed, with 'FEAR of dying'! All fears are located in the base chakra, as will become clearer later.

At the time of the operation I was only four years old, and bringing up blood by the bucketful afterwards was an absolute nightmare. This could have been one of the reasons why I did not like to believe the doctors that there was 'nothing to worry about' and that everything was 'very much routine' when they tried to encourage me to go ahead with the gallbladder operation. No thank you! Not if I could help it! Plus, I had read a testimony of case histories in a health magazine, reporting on research of gallbladder problems and the removal of the organ. The university team conducting the research had followed patients for over 20 years or more after the removal of the gallbladder and found that a much higher percentage suffered from duodenal cancer 20-25 years after the operation, compared to people who still had their gallbladder. Unfortunately I do not know which university in Germany carried out the research as I did not keep the article at the time, nor the magazine, yet that was enough information for me to seek out an alternative treatment 27 years ago, which led me to Homœopathy in the first place. Coming back to the previous paragraph I would like to add that I disliked being 'blocked in the bowels'. But help was at hand with the **BOWEL NOSODES**.

The Second Step: The Link to the Chakras

After qualifying at LCH (London College of Homœopathy) I joined the Guild of Homœopaths for further studies.

During the first few months with the Guild we learnt new remedies and related them to the **chakras** (more about the chakras later) with great enthusiasm. During a case discussion where we applied our knowledge of the new and old remedies, including the Miasms and chakras, a very brief discussion about where the **Bowel Nosodes** would fit in and how they too have their place in the 'chakra system' followed.

It is difficult to describe the feeling of suddenly becoming a 'knower'; it was as if someone had switched a light on in my head, a kind of 'eureka' moment. Suddenly it all made sense and I could not wait for our summer break to work out my table of the Bowel Nosodes! I just had to put it down on paper in order to share it with my friends and colleagues. And finally now, by including it in this book, I can share it with more people and I hope that everyone will find it very useful and a wonderful shortcut to the Bowel Nosodes and the associated remedies.

I have worked on the table again and again, and there is still room to put in your own observations and increase your personal knowledge on the Bowel Nosodes. As far as I am aware there has not been a proving in the traditional way for most of these Nosodes, thus the observations have come mainly from their clinical use.

Step Three: Predispositions in the Eyes

My third reason for being so convinced about using the Bowel Nosodes was my sudden interest in IRIDOLOGY. Marion Joyce, a Homœopath from Chelmsford who attended the Guild with me, had looked into my eyes on my request to check my iris. It was truly amazing what she could tell from just viewing my iris!

Due to her excellent diagnostic skills I was hooked. I now wanted to learn this art of 'Gentle Diagnosis', too. If we think of Homœopathy as the 'Gentle Art of Healing' then this seemed to complement it perfectly. With a magnifying lens and a torch it is a very quick way to learn about the patients' 'problems', even before they have opened their mouth.

Of course, this does not mean that I do not let the patients 'pour out' their problems, as the case taking can also be part of the healing. During seminars I admired Rajan Sankaran's case-taking and I almost feel that he no longer needed to give a remedy, as he had gone so deep with his patients by talking that they arrived at the root of their mental/ emotional problems. By being asked again and again about their feelings and finding out their **biggest fears** (remember fears are base chakra issues), or talking abstractly in the third person, the patient comes up with answers and 'key-words', which give wonderful clues to the remedies they need. All this talking is digging into the deepest levels of the being and is very healing itself. According to the lectures of Sankaran in these cases the potencies of 200c and above are very appropriate when working on the emotional or mental level. However, my own ideas about potencies will be discussed in the appendix. As Homœopaths we all have our own style; we have all learnt to be good listeners and keen observers. For me to then be able to add extra information by checking the iris is just great.

An example is from a recent consultation I gave: A mother came with her grown daughter who looked fairly relaxed during the case taking, is extremely intelligent, and certainly did not let on about 'internal tension'. But, I could see this when checking her eyes. (The eyes are known as the **'mirror of the soul'** – so the saying goes.)

I said something like: 'according to your irises you appear to be very tense at times'. The mother just laughed and said: 'That is the understatement of the year'. It certainly broke the ice, we had a good laugh, and it gave valuable clues to the remedies needed, especially the Bowel Nosodes, as the tightness was seen in the area of the intestines.

Iridology can also help to dispel FEARS in people when you tell them that they have basically a strong constitution as noted from the iris, yet they are great worriers, especially about their health! When asked about their fears people often deny that they have any, yet at the same time tell you that they have annual health checks, including x-rays 'just in case' the doctor should overlook any signs or symptoms. They want to have it in 'black and white' on the x-ray picture that there is nothing inside the body that has not been detected so far. Until they have the results of the hospital or doctor they are often 'stressed' due to fears.

A strong constitution is of course not always the case and imperfections can be pointed out and explained. These are inherited weaknesses as well as traumas from accidents, or self inflicted by toxins like smoking or too much alcohol to name just two.

Coming back to the issue of fears, other fears can be about their job and of what the future might bring, with special worries about their family. All of these anxieties can block the Base Chakra, creating health problems in the long run. Living on coffee and fast food, or just snacks or 'comfort food', as a way to calm the nerves does not really work. It merely adds to the problems of adrenal exhaustion and the dilemma for the pancreas of hyper and hypoglycaemia.

In the chakra system the CROWN is at the opposite end from the BASE and of course reflects what goes on in the Base. The CROWN and the THIRD EYE are the centres of WISDOM, yet we would not call it wise to indulge in comfort foods like chocolates and sweets. An Argentum Nitricum state full of worries, to name just one remedy here, goes with the upper chakras. Sulphur and Phosphor, part of our building blocks for the physical body and the minerals are very much associated with the Base Chakra, are also required to curb the cravings and help people to feel secure and 'at home' on this planet.

A perfect example: Looking at the rubric 'Sweets desires', lists three Nosodes: Carcinosin, Medorrhinum, and Tuberculinum; as well as three Bowel Nosodes: Dysentery-co. for the Brow Chakra, Proteus for the Heart Chakra, and Morgan for the Base. **The anxiety taking place in the head usually starts in the base**, causing a blockage, moves up via the heart and weakens the body, 'undermining health'. This can be seen just by looking at the three Bowel Nosodes and placing them into the Chakra system with the related remedies.

In the Western World England is known as a 'sweet nation', with very high sugar consumption. Since the pancreas is all about being 'positive for the future', if a 'created' problem can be seen from all that 'sugary stuff' in the iris it is very important to talk to people about their diet. A 'sweet tooth' can be clearly detected by **orange discolouring** in the centre of the iris and is not restricted to adults, but sadly can be seen in young children, too. Equally, 'lacunas' (the Latin word for holes or pits) may often be observed in the iris at the positions of the pancreas, signs pointing to a weakness and possible problems in the future.

I would like to tell you here about a case where the 'warning' worked a treat. The husband of a former school friend of mine in Germany had black-outs at work and had been to hospital, where he had undergone all the check-ups possible; yet the doctors could not see what could possibly be wrong with him. NOTHING was found!

I looked into his eyes and checked his irises. Immediately I had the answers! Using a small concave mirror that allows a person to see their own irises I was able to show him and his wife my findings. I explained what could be seen and why I was saying this and that about his organs and the meaning of colours seen in the iris.

Her husband has very clear, almost piercing, blue eyes and according to the fibres a very strong constitution. Had it not been for the markings in the 'pancreatic corners' I would have wondered what could possibly be wrong with him. Here an almost 'square-shaped' Autonomic Nerve Wreath (ANW; will be discussed later) could clearly be seen, which I pointed out to the patient and explained that the pancreas was waving the 'red flag' at him and asking for help. During the consultation, I asked about his diet and it turned out that if he started a bar of chocolate he would not stop until it was finished; his wife immediately told him off for this, saying 'I told you so!'

That is not to say that I would not have arrived at a similar conclusion by taking the case traditionally, without using iridology, as it turned out that his brother had recently been diagnosed with diabetes! The signs in the iris were warning him that he was in a pre-diabetic state and a change of eating habit, for one thing, was very much needed.

Pointing this out to his wife, she took it on board more than he did, totally changing their diet and banning him from sweets and chocolates. The next time I saw her (accidentally, whilst shopping in town) **she** had lost weight and looked stunning with her new figure after a total change of diet for both her and her husband. She told me that her husband was fine and no further treatment was needed. Well, if the wife says so, she must be right; he had no say in this! (You can make up your own mind about a German 'Hausfrau'!)

During the initial consultation he had immediately agreed to a course of remedies, which included Bowel Nosodes, and with the help of the Nosodes I am sure it was easier for him to change his diet, too, as they greatly help to lower the sweet cravings. Jokingly, I always say from now on that the only sweets they are allowed to have are the little 'sugar pills' that I give them. (Unless they prefer the chalk tablets, which I give to people who are suddenly afraid of sugar when suffering from diabetes and need to be more careful: Well, we can accommodate all tastes and needs.)

This, my third reason for my enthusiasm of the Bowel Nosodes, is much longer in its explanation than the previous two, but I would like you to get a real feeling and a good taster of Iridology. My fascination for every iris I see is immense, as you never see two irises looking the same. Even from the same person, the left and right iris can look very different, giving wonderful clues as to which side of the family the 'weakness' might come from (with the left side being the mother's medical family history; and the right iris, the father's). Like searching the family background with the Miasm, the irises allow us to spot at a glance inherited problems. It always astonishes patients when a disease (or predisposition to one) can be allocated as coming from the mother's or father's side of the family, making such findings all the more interesting for both the patient and the Homœopath.

Northern Europeans, with blond or brown hair and blue eyes, are always so much easier to diagnose than those with brown eyes. I often have to tell brown-eyed people of the white Caucasian race that their eyes should really be blue and this was the eye colour they were born with! They are usually put off by the idea that their true eye colour is blue, especially when they have lovely hazel coloured brown eyes, or seem to have enchanting 'Scarlet O'Hara' green eyes. (Indeed my own eyes are green, although I would rather they where blue again.) My younger sister has brown eyes, yet being ten years older than her I can still remember her wonderful blue eyes at birth. Within the first two years of her life, however, they changed to dark brown and then an almost black colour and everyone thought that she was taking after my mother who had 'brown' eyes! (Not naturally brown, as you might have guessed by now). They were certainly not **real** or **true** brown eyes, as found in the Asian or African races. In fact, only a very small proportion of the world's population have blue eyes; the vast majority of eyes are brown, in different shades to a very dark (almost black) and almost velvety appearance. **No strands of fibres**, as seen in a blue iris, can be detected in such dark-coloured eyes. However, if you do observe these strands in a brown or black iris, like in a typical 'tubercular' iris of blue-eyed people, and you ask about the family history, it most likely turns out that they had a Caucasian ancestor somewhere in the not-too-distant past.

I have had great fun with this statement when checking one of my Japanese friend's husband's irises. Her husband did not have the typical dark brown iris Japanese people have and the 'truth' was revealed! I was told that his grandfather had indeed been a white Russian, if I remember rightly. Everyone is always fascinated about what can be detected in the iris. (All the same, one might have to be careful about certain findings and statements, depending on to whom one is talking.)

In a true brown iris with its velvety surface one has to look for discolouring, just like in blue eyes, but with different shadings. The lacunas (lesions or pockets) are in places of organ weakness; no matter which colour iris we are talking about. Ballooning in the bowels can be seen clearly, and tightness points to strictures or a prolapse of part of the intestines. (Even the removal of the whole of the large colon is evident in the iris, as I observed in a colon cancer patient once.)

Recounting another case of a Japanese friend's relative who I was asked to 'check-out', I began by viewing his irises. From looking at the irises I told him that his current problem had started in the sigmoid colon! With this, the gentlemen jumped up and fetched a photograph, showing me the tumour that had been removed from the sigmoid colon the previous year. Next, seeing quite a 'marking' in the lung area and looking at his finger nails, which were typically 'spoon-shaped', I enquired if he had ever suffered from tuberculosis (TB), which he denied. Yet, as soon as he left the room for a minute, his wife told me that he had TB when he was about 30 (he was now well in his 70s).

To my surprise he still smoked, so I asked his wife why he had not been asked to stop smoking. 'No, why?' was the answer; the doctors had never told him that he had TB! They just gave him medication, so he could see no reason at the time to give up his cigarettes. (Well, I guess 40 years ago things were different about informing the patient about the 'dis-ease' they had.)

Further checks revealed that the liver was very toxic, with the liver region of the iris being much lighter in colour than the rest of the iris. I pointed this out to his family (who

17

were all present at the consultation) and they were all amazed, since only the previous week or so his doctor had given him a clear diagnosis of liver cancer. The family was told that the cancer cells from the sigmoid colon must already have spread to the liver before it had been removed and that there was little chance for him to live much longer than 6 months. Having been able to diagnose the main problem areas so quickly from the iris the family was most impressed and felt that they could trust me, even if they had never heard about Homœopathy before and what these little sugar pills could do. Unfortunately in this case, it was too late even for Homœopathy to make a 'turn around' and the gentleman in question died very peacefully at home a few weeks later.

A little more about my own observations as to why blue eyes might change colour: Coming back to my sister's brown eyes, which you will remember she did not have when she was born, I feel that one reason for the change of colour within the first two years of her life could have come about by being given 'formula milk', as was in vogue at the time. (It was supposed to be better than the mother's breast milk – can you believe it?)

Another reason could have been that, at a very young age, she was given too many Antibiotics – which were given for everything as the new 'wonder drug' after World War II – for recurrent tonsillitis and later cystitis. If I were to give my sister a 'homœopathic label' she was certainly a 'Silicea' child who did not thrive and would have done well on 'Gaertner'; the children's Nosode – more about that later when we come to the throat chakra!

My mother, too, had 'brown' eyes, as mentioned earlier, yet both of her parents had blue eyes. I remember my grandparents' eyes well and in my mother's case **the brown of the iris pointed to 'liver' problems** (she had her gall-bladder removed) and numerous other problems, which resulted in her death aged only 58. In general terms one can say that a brown iris in a blue-eyed person is due to liver and gall-bladder problems, amongst others. (A **gall-bladder** problem on its own is seen more in **orange** discolouration, as well as suggesting **pancreatic** problems). This, I guess, was one of the reasons why I studied Homœopathy and Iridology; it was a CALLING, to heal myself as well as helping the rest of my family. It was not for fear of dying young, more the fear of suffering great pain; every time I have had a gall-bladder colic I had a good 'taste' of terrible pain.

This section introduced iridology as a further reason of my interest in the Bowel Nosodes and has given you a brief taster of the practice of iridology. In the next chapter I would like to give a more informative overview of this magnificent method of diagnosis. (Computer programmes too have been created to help with the diagnosis nowadays.)

Chapter TWO — Iridology and the Intestines

Introduction to Iridology

Iris-diagnosis is nothing 'brand new'! It was not long after Homœopathy was rediscovered by Dr Samuel Hahnemann that another doctor rediscovered this **'gentle way of diagnoses'**. (Incidentally, when I write that Homœopathy was rediscovered by Hahnemann I am referring to his ventures of studying ancient writings. Hahnemann was a true genius and spoke many modern languages, but also the classical old languages. Thus he was able to resource his writings from a wide range, where no doubt he found that the Egyptians used 'energy medicine' with remedies very familiar to any homœopath nowadays).

Returning to the study of the iris, Dr Ignaz von Peczely, born on 26th January 1826 (and died in 1911), can be named a 'father' and 'founder' of our modern Iridology. He drew the first iris topography, with these original findings being published in a book with the title 'Entdeckung auf dem Gebiete der Natur und Heilkunde – Anleitung zum Studium der Diagnose aus dem Auge', which translates to 'Discoveries in the field of natural health and healing – Instructions for studying diagnosis from the eye'. These topographies have been modified since their first publication in 1881 and now there are about 30 different versions of the first 'iris-map', although these do not all differ totally in their presentation.

Dr von Peczely had only a very simple magnifying glass and nothing like the magnification we have at our disposal today, yet his keen observations and endless checking and comparing iris markings with health problems of the patients produced the first charts.

Going further back in history, Hippocrates (460-375 BC), too, was fascinated by the eyes. To him they did not only represent the 'Window to the Soul', but he was convinced that the colour of the iris and the sclera (the white of the eye) act like 'a mirror to the organs' and could give indications of diseases, adding valuable points to the study of the Four Humours (Lymphatic system).

We now know that discolouring of a blue iris to green or brown, which is not the 'natural' colour (as discussed earlier), does indeed point to changes within the body. As mentioned before, toxicity or the overuse of antibiotics can be one of the reasons for the discolouration. Environmental factors can be another reason: For example if a person's constitution is weak amalgam fillings in their teeth can have an impact; years of exposure from working with chemicals, such as those used in the 'dry cleaning' business, could illustrate lung and kidney impairments; and I will not even enter the debate on mobile phones and their impact on the energy bodies! I just wanted to name just a few environmental issues which could be classed as 'harmful' to a healthy body.

The Greek philosopher Aristotle (384-322 BC) noted that 'blue' is the colour of the iris of all newborn, which of course can only be applied to Caucasians. Even before this time, more than 3,000 years ago, the Chaldeans are known to have read 'diseases from the eyes'.

These are just a few historical facts about the earliest Iridology. In more recent times Pastor Emanuel Felke (1858-1926) carried on where von Peczely left off. He prepared Homœopathic remedies, which he then prescribed according to his findings of the iris diagnosis of his patients. As his title 'Pastor' suggests, he was not a doctor. However, whilst still a student at University, he loved listening to lectures on science and medicine, as well as studying theology. Thus he came across the study of the iris and diagnosing diseases. His fame as a diagnostician in this art and his abilities to heal people spread from Germany across its borders. Unfortunately, he never wrote his findings down and most of the knowledge we have of his practices come from a book published by one of his students, called 'The Eye-diagnosis based upon the principles of Pastor Felke'.

Another Pastor, by the name of Nils Liljequist, was interested in finding a connection between the organs and the signs in the iris. He, too, published a book on his discoveries in 1893 called 'Diagnose aus den Augen' (Diagnosis from the eyes). In fact, he was the first to describe **drug poisoning** signs in the iris, since he had observed his own iris changing colour from a clear blue to a 'green with orange in it' after the drug quinine was giving to him when he was young. At the age of fourteen he suddenly began to have health problems soon after being vaccinated. From being a healthy teenager the lymph glands in his neck swelled after the vaccination and he developed polyps, which were treated with quinine. The polyps were surgically removed and iodine was applied externally! He was only twenty years old when he published a paper telling the World that 'Quinine and iodine changed the colour of my irises'.

More recently, in 1954, a researcher found a connection between the nerves and the organs of the body, as seen in the iris. In Germany, Josef Deck, the founder of the Institute of Iris Diagnosis in Ettlingen, needs to be mentioned, as he is recognised as an eminent researcher on the subject and has published several books, one called 'Grundlagen der Irisdiagnostik' (Principles of Iris Diagnosis), which remains one of the most prominent in this discipline.

Another very outstanding Iridologist of the last Century was Dr Bernard Jensen Ph.D., who has published numerous books containing coloured photographs of various irises, which the very early books did not have, containing only 'drawn iris pictures'. (However, if no camera is at hand, quick sketches can be a useful way to record one's findings.) Cameras are of course ideal to see improvements after treatment, although this is often disputed and I am not yet experienced enough to argue with eminent Iridologists who have much more expertise than I have. However, I still believe that the iris can change with Homeopathic treatment, as I have seen this happen from my own limited experience.

I remember one student of Homœopathy who wanted to learn about the Bowel Nosodes and, as it transpired, needed them badly herself as she was 'hooked on sugar'! This showed up as an 'orange colouring' in the bowel area of the iris! We discussed which remedies she would benefit from and here came my surprise: When we met two or three months later she was very proud and very happy to show me that all the orange in her iris had gone! She told me that she had 'cleared out the bowels', had stopped eating cakes etc., and supported the pancreas with remedies, thus was no longer craving sweets either. She had lost weight and her iris was a brilliant blue again. This is just one case that springs to mind in which a student took everything I had said about the Bowel-flora on board and achieved the required result herself. (Remember: Orange colouring in a blue iris points to pancreas problems.)

The books on Iridology available on the market now are too numerous to mention. By giving a little 'taster' about the history of Iridology and how, with a good magnifying glass and a torch, it can help to see what is going on in the body, I hope I can create an appetite for further studies. With the aid of these simple tools the most noticeable problems seen appear to be situated in, or coming from, the bowels. In fact, other alternative health systems agree that 'death comes via the bowels – very slowly' as one headline read in a German health magazine a couple of years ago. A lecture on Tibetan Medicine by Dr Tsewang Tamdin that I attended recently confirmed my understanding of this slow death of the body, since it was highlighted that all disease starts with **'indigestion'** of some sort.

When it comes to indigestion/constipation/parasites in the gut, etc., the idea of enemas was nothing out of the ordinary in Germany, whilst in England it almost seemed the 'unspeakable' as a way of keeping the bowels moving. Anyway, when I was a child this method of enemas would be 'administered' to us (reluctant) children by my mother if there we had any sort of bowel problem. This way we grew up believing that it was important to keep the bowels 'clean'. These days we have a new word for it: 'Colonic Irrigation'!

Keeping the bowels clean is very much in vogue now, with colonic irrigation as well as companies advertising and selling 'healthy bacteria' in the form of 'active' yoghurts. From this we are much more aware of the important role of the bowels. I always like to compare the bowels with **'the kitchen in a house'**, from which the body is fed with all the nutrients, vitamins and minerals needed to keep us fit and healthy. Imagine a cold and dirty kitchen with very little cooking taking place: I am sure you would feel that a house with a 'cold' kitchen is **not** a friendly house and one that you would not like to visit too often! On the other hand, a house with an old fashion type Aga cooker, for example, with alluring smells of good food is inviting and you would like to stay and revisit as often as possible; the same goes for the bowels. If the bowel flora is unhealthy the body cannot be sustained indefinitely and consequently the **SPIRIT** wants to leave and go HOME to the Spirit World where it came from. One last word here: What ends up as waste products from the body should not smell 'foul', but pleasant, if at all. Any mother who has breastfed her baby will know just too well how very little smell comes from the nappies when changing the baby, unless of course the mother has a dreadful diet herself.

Introduction to the Intestines

The Small Intestine

- The small intestine is a TUBE that averages about 2.5cm in diameter.
- It is divided into 3 segments:
  1. **Duodenum**; the shortest part – starts at the pyloric sphincter of the stomach
  2. **Jejunum**; together with the above = 40%
  3. **Ileum**; the longest part = 60% – joins the large intestine at the ileocaecal sphincter
- The walls of the small intestine are composed of the same 4 layers as most of the gastro-intestinal (GI) tract.
- The mucosa consists of microvillus, giving it a velvety appearance. These villi are able to cope with 12 litres of intestinal contents (food, water and secretion) per day. They not only aid absorption and digestion of nutrition, but also cause the chyme, the semi-liquid mass of food and gastric juices passing from the stomach to the intestine, to spiral rather than move in a straight line.
- The life of a mucosal cell is 2-5 days.
- Chemical digestion depends not only on its own secretion, but also on the activity of the liver/gallbladder (bile) and the pancreas (pancreatic juice). These are added in the duodenum. The chyme from the jejunum normally contains few, if any, bacteria; the rapid transit of the chyme and the gastric acids may inhibit bacterial growth in this region.
- The distance from the pylorus to the ileocaecal valve is generally about 285cm (or 2.85 m); however, at autopsy this distance has been reported to be as long as 700cm (7 m).

The SMALL INTESTINES are seen in both eyes within the Autonomic Nerve Wreath (ANW) of the Iris.

in the right eye	= from 1 to 5 o'clock
in the left eye	= from 7 to 11 o'clock

The Large Intestine

- The large intestine is a TUBE of 6.5cm diameter.
- It starts from the ileum in the right iliac fossa (with the caecum).
  (The ileocaecal sphincter allows material to pass from the small into large intestine.)
- It is divided into four principal regions:
  1. **Caecum**; the appendix is attached here
  2. **Colon**; the largest part of the large intestine
  3. **Rectum**; the last part before it terminates in the…
  4. **Anal canal**; 2-3cm long
- A healthy large intestine is typically about 150cm (1.5 m) long. However, there have been cases reported from autopsies, where it had stretched to twice this size to 300cm (3 m).

- While the first part of the digestion is an enzymatic action, the last stage occurs through bacteria.

- Up to 40 % of faecal mass is bacteria. – **These Bacteria will be my special foci**. In a healthy colon the bacteria should ideally be **85% Lacto bacteria** and no more than **15 % Coli-form bacteria**. This is exactly the reverse in modern society showing only **15% Lacto bacteria** and a monstrous **85% Coli-form** and other types of putrefactive bacteria, producing *indole* and *skatol* giving the faeces the foul smelling odour. The 'friendly' lacto bacteria and bifida bacteria are health enhancing, but are no longer present in large quantities in the majority of people the way they should be. No wonder people often feel 'fatigued'. This could be one reason why they might come to seek help, as this would cause 'tired blood', as so many minerals and vitamins (especially the B Vitamins made in the gut) are missing or so very low in numbers that the body has not got the energy to 'repair' itself. Most of the time the body is too busy trying to detoxify itself.

- These bacteria ferment any remaining carbohydrates and release hydrogen, carbon dioxide, and methane gas, which contribute to flatus in the colon.

- Several vitamins are needed for normal metabolism, including some B Vitamins and Vitamin K. Depression can result if the B vitamins are lacking, while Vitamin K could be called a 'wonder healer', helping to heal wounds, renew bones and give vitality until old age. It needs oil to be assimilated in the intestines and therefore fresh salads with pure olive oil on a daily basis can help to stay young.

- The chyme remains in the large intestine for 3 to 10 hours while it becomes solid or semi-solid as a result of absorption, when it becomes known as faeces.

- Digestion of food: the first part of a meal reaches the caecum in about 4 hours, with all of the undigested portions entering the colon within 8 or 9 hours. On average, the first remnants of the meal reach the hepatic flexure in 6 hours, the splenic flexure in 9 hours, and the pelvic colon in 12 hours. From the pelvic colon to the anus, transport is much slower. During one study of how long food needs to go through the digestive tract as much as 25% of the residue of a test meal was found to be in the rectum after 72 hours. (That is, indeed, a 'lazy bowel'.)

- Faeces consists of inorganic salts, bacteria and sloughed off epithelial cells from the mucosa of the GI tract, plus undigested parts of food and water. Some figures regarding the composition of faeces from an average diet:

> 75% water and 25% solids: Of the solids 30% are bacteria, 15% inorganic salts/material (mostly calcium and phosphates), and 5% fat and fat deviates; the other 50% is cellulose and other indigestible fibre.

Only the colon contains large numbers of bacteria. At birth the colon is sterile, but the intestinal flora becomes established in the first six months; a further reason why breastfeeding is very important as it helps to generate a healthy gut flora.

The LARGE INTESTINE is seen in both eyes within the ANW:

Right eye: The first part the **caecum** is seen from 5 o'clock, with the **appendix** at 6.30, joining the **ascending colon** at about 8 o'clock (where the liver and gallbladder would be located, too). In the body the colon turns right (where it meets the liver under the ribcage) to become the **transverse colon**, seen in the iris from 11 to 1 o'clock (where the mesentery glands are also located in the iris). (The mesentery glands are lymphatic vessels that supply the large and small intestines and can become inflamed, especially in young children after a sore throat or chest infection, causing abdominal pain.)

Left eye: Starting at 11 o'clock with the **transverse colon** it runs downward (where it meets the spleen in the body), to become the **descending colon**. Past 4 o'clock (where the spleen is located in the eye), it turns at the splenic flexure to be called **sigmoid**; seen from 5 to 6.30. Here, it will be located in the iris, between the kidney and the vagina or prostate, at about 6.45 as **rectum/anus**. The sigmoid and rectum areas always need to be scrutinised as these are the most common sides for colon cancer.

The Autonomic Nerve Wreath

Some facts about the gut and its relationship to the Autonomic Nerve Wreath (ANW) and the bowel flora.

In the developing embryo of only 25 days the neural tube is clearly visible next to the TUBE of the bowels, which at this stage is called the **foregut, midgut** and **hindgut**. The close connection between these two tubes is reflected in the eyes by an inner ring around the pupil, covering about one third of the iris. The ANW connects the area of the gut to the organs showing how well the adjoining organs are supplied with nerve signals. A broken wreath here may indicate a trauma, which can lead the iridologist to a further line of questioning during a consultation. Recently, I asked one of my patients about any previous trauma seen age 5-6 by a broken ANW, she is now in her thirties. She was amazed that I could tell and replied that as a child she had been in a car accident with her parents and her sister. The car had caught fire and her sister still bears the scars. Another example is from a patient who had a 'stain' in the spleen area of her iris and a broken ANW on the opposite side. When I asked further about this I was told that the spleen had ruptured during a car crash when she was younger and needed to be taken out immediately. Iridology is the study, based on this link, of the nervous system and the connection of the organs to the gut and stomach ring in the centre of the iris, indicating how well they are functioning? Therefore when looking at 'stains or discolouration' in the gut area showing an unhealthy bowel it is easy to see why they are suffering.

Often when asking the patients about their 'digestive system', and enquiring of any problems they may have, most will say: 'No problem', unless of course this was the very reason for the visit, like suffering from Crohn's disease, IBS (very much in fashion these days as a diagnosis by the doctor), or similar 'rushing' of the stool. They do not like to readily admit to flatulence, but the iris will tell a different story, indicating ballooning and pockets in the bowels. Sometimes, these pockets are filled with pus and debris, (again pus itself cannot be seen) which can settle and accumulate to such a degree that the colon's circumference expands to four or more times its normal size. This can clearly be seen in the iris by the ANW being 'pushed' halfway across the iris, with 'Lacunas' (openings/gaps in the fibres) jutting 'into' the organs positioned in the iris adjacent to the bowels. (Glandular fever in teenage years or in adults could have been one of the causes for these conditions). Medically speaking, these pockets are known as diverticulosis.

Regarding CONSTIPATION, people often have no idea how 'abnormal' their 'normal' stool is. It should take **as little as 24 hours** for the food to pass through the gastrointestinal (GI) tract; about 8 hours through the stomach and small intestine, and the rest of the time in the colon. Yet, in our Western Civilisation it is more like **65-100 hours.** As a consequence old faeces may build up layers of coating on the lining of the gut, which may run the entire length of the colon (the small intestine, too). Parasites (of which there are <u>over 134 different kinds</u>; not a very pleasant thought at all), can thrive in this filthy environment, as well as CANDIDA (a fungus).

Regarding parasites, I would like to mention Dr Hulda R. Clarke, who has written wonderful books about such a dire subject that are well worth reading. Candida, another huge problem in our modern society, is seen as a **Radii solaris,** giving the appearance of a pleated skirt to the iris and 'castling' (small lines giving the appearance of castles along the edge of the pupil) if not so severe. The fungus Candida albicans causes mycosis, which appears as 'nappy rash' in babies, as thrush of the mouth in young children, or later as athletes' foot, as well as crippling the nails. Additionally it can affect the lungs, the intestine, and of course the sexual organs. Candida thrives anywhere in the body where it is moist and warm. Vulvae candidiasis is not restricted to females and can be sexually transmitted, with the male suffering 'balanitis', which is an inflammation of the head of the penis. Usually the healthy bacteria in the body can keep any fungal infection in check, especially the healthy bacteria in the bowels. However, disorder like diabetes mellitus, can make the condition worse, as too can hormonal changes during pregnancy. This would be a very good reason to go on a 'clear-out-programme', including the bowel-flora programme, before planning a baby in order to improve one's own health, as well as giving the baby the best start in life.

An unhealthy bowel-flora not only creates 'gas' – which we pass every 30 minutes, according to a recent university study that I heard about on the radio; not very lady or gentlemen like – but also stretches the bowels to the extent that 'sagging' occurs, especially in the transverse colon. This prolapse of the transverse colon allows the stomach (which can be seen in the eyes directly surrounding the pupil) to assume a 'fishhook shape', which in turn harbours acids and gases that produce belching, etc. A sagging transverse colon puts pressure on the uterus and bladder, leading to a need to urinate more frequently. Additionally, toxicity in the transverse colon is often indicated if there is a 'sinus' disturbance, i.e. constant catarrh. Sinusitis needs the Bowel Nosodes Morgan Pure, as well as Sycotic Co., as will become clearer later.

I will not detail here any disturbances in the **mental** area that a 'sagging' part of the bowels will cause, as this is a topic in its own right. However, I will mention that this would be seen in both eyes from 11 – 1 o'clock. Although, I would like to comment here that the **Bowel Nosodes** will of course help the 'mental' problems, too. A 'dropped' transverse colon is more often seen in the 'daisy-petal' iris, indicating weak connective tissue throughout the body. (The calcium metabolism needs to be checked, thus the thyroid and parathyroid located at 2.30 in the right and 9.30 in the left eye have to be scrutinised.)

One other 'symptom' a patient might admit to is 'body odour', which is in close relation to intestinal putrefaction, especially 'foot odour' (**not only** due to the trainers worn so often these days on a daily basis by children). When clearing up the bowels the 'sweaty' feet will improve, although the underarm odour unfortunately is the last to go. I once heard of a young lady in Japan who had the sweat-glands removed while still a teenager, as she 'suffered' from her **own** body odour (physically and mentally). Ever since then she has had a constantly blocked nose; not the right solution to 'remove' body odour, for sure.

Signs of excess acidity in the stomach to look out for in the iris are the colours of the stomach/bowel area. In a blue iris these are easier to see for obvious reasons, as mentioned before. Should a blue iris be **very white**, for example, this indicates 'over-acidity' that could lead to ulceration of both organs. In a true brown iris this acidity would be seen as 'yellow'. The old belief to drink plenty of milk to 'calm' the ulcer would be totally wrong as dairy foods tend to produce mucus, thus increase acidity. In any case, too much of our modern food is acid forming. These acid-forming foods add to the 'unpleasant smells' expelled from the body. Apart from the smelly body odour created when the **acids** combine with the body fluids, they additionally create the typical picture of 'burn-out', which can be seen in Homœopathic remedies like **Phosphoric Acid, Nitric Acid** or **Picric Acid** and **Sulphuric Acid** (in the last remedy alcohol could be the reason for the demise in health), to name the big four. Other acids like **Benzoic Acid** give an indication of gout. Here, the acids cause periodic pains in the small joints, and the urine is offensive and has a strong 'foul smell' (which of course the remedy picture of Nitric Acid has too). An excess of the well-known **Lactic acid**, produced by vigorous exercise, can lead to cramp and in the worst scenario, to a heart attack. Normally, lactic acid derives from the breakdown of glycogen, or is produced during the digestive process by the action of bacterium on lactose (lactic acid causes the souring of milk), and is removed from the blood by the liver. Should it accumulate in the body, we have the condition called **'Acidosis'**, which causes rheumatic pains and nausea, especially in pregnancy, with early morning sickness and copious foot-sweat, which is a feature of the proving of lactic acid. However, in this case the foot-sweat is **not** offensive. We could expect all symptoms mentioned to arise from increased acidity in the body having gone into a 'sour' state.

If the ANW is not clearly seen in the eyes (very faint outlines), it can be concluded that no suitable digestion is taking place. Similarly, a **'red' inner ring**, which is most often very clearly visible – sometimes only in parts along the side of the pupil and at other times all the way round – indicates that assimilation of Minerals/Vitamins is **not** happening. This will automatically lead to nutritional deficiencies. Pernicious anaemia of the blood is just one to be mentioned, which could result from the unhealthy bowel flora and lack of Vitamin B.

A sluggish lymphatic system can be clearly seen in the iris as small clusters of **white tophi** at the edge of the iris when an acute illness, like influenza, is present. Should this become a more chronic condition these tophi vary from dirty yellow to almost brown (as I recently observed in one of my patients who had come after a chemotherapy treatment). Eventually, the immune-system will no longer be able to cope and the tophi will move further into the centre, i.e. 'closer to the organs', rather than staying at the edge of the iris.

When examining an iris using a torch and a magnifying lens the pupils should naturally contract, which is an automatic reaction called **Myosis**. However, this is not always the case for a variety of reasons. It can be caused either by taking eye-drops (for example, Belladonna) or drug use, either prescribed or 'pleasure' drugs, both of which may result in these side effects. I have observed this effect several times in young people and during the case taking some admitted to having 'tried' certain drugs. However, they were not aware of the effect it has on the eyes and the associated systems such as the sympathetic nervous system, which can be seen in the right eye, and the parasympathetic system, which is located in the left eye (and which is usually worse affected from drug intake). Another reason for lack of myosis (when no drugs have been taken) is simply a 'hyper' adrenal state, or adrenal exhaustion (hypo), of the person, again checking the right and the left iris.

An abnormal enlargement of the pupil is called **Mydriasis** can be added to the list of symptoms that aid searching for the right remedies. In fact, under the heading of **'Eyes'** and **'Pupil'**, the medical repertory has wonderful rubrics of 'contracted', 'dilated', 'irregular', 'unequal' and 'insensitive to light', with remedies like Belladonna, Hyoscyamus and Opium high on the list of remedies to choose from.

When the pupil is enlarged, apart from being photophobic, other 'shapes' in the pupil can sometimes be observed too. Examples are from **vertical ovals** indicating serious pathology, and other 'ovals' pointing in various directions, all indicating different problems. Another 'shape' that needs to be taken very seriously is a **square ANW,** as mentioned earlier in the case of the pre-diabetic friend in Germany.

In the 'mixed-biliary' iris, as the name biliary suggests, we are looking at problems of the liver and gall-bladder – showing colours of green, light-to-yellow-brown, and most likely light blue showing through, being the true colour of the iris; the whole stomach/bowel area is usually of the brown colouring of various shades. The Bowel Nosodes Morgan Pure and Morgan Bach, which address 'congestion in the liver', would be particularly appropriate to start with to address this kind of problem.

As with the bowels, the small and large intestines are easily identified organs in every patient's iris, providing much information about the patient's state of dis-ease. I have researched the Bowel Nosodes for many years now and treated patients very successfully by changing their bowel-flora. Once this has taken place, the patient is much more likely to adopt a much healthier diet, which is vital to good health. When thinking about the Bowel Nosodes we must, of course, talk about the man who gave them to us: Dr Edward Bach.

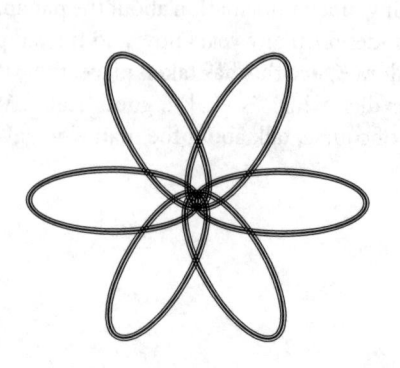

Chapter THREE

The emergence of the Bowel Nosodes – Introducing Dr Edward Bach

Born 24th September 1886 near Birmingham, UK
(43 years after Hahnemann's death)

Edward Bach was apparently a delicate baby needing much care yet grew stronger as he grew older. In 1906 he started his medical training at Birmingham University and later moved to University College Hospital in London to continue his medical studies, where he graduated in 1912. At his graduation he is supposed to have stated that it would take him five years to 'forget everything he had been taught'.

It is reported that he rarely left London from the day he entered university until 1930 when he went to the countryside on a journey of discovery, in search of the now world-wide known Bach Flower Essences. These Essences were intended to replace the seven bacterial Nosodes, which he had researched and found so valuable in restoring his patients' health. Personally I feel they can complement each other, as both can be linked to the chakras; but more about that later.

It was after his graduation whilst working at University College Hospital that he became very interested in vaccination/bacteriology, and immunology in particular. The research that Bach was conducting at the hospital led him to examine the bowel flora of the large colon. He found that certain micro-organisms that were naturally present in the large intestine were present in elevated numbers in the sick. Thus he considered the possibility that most chronic diseases were the result of auto-intoxication from the bowels.

These intestinal germs belong to the **non-lactose fermenting, gram-negative group.** Bach utilised these bacteria as vaccines to cure chronic illness; this was the beginning of the **Bowel Nosodes**, although at that time he was still <u>injecting the vaccine</u>, which was prepared from the killed cultures of the organisms.

Incidentally, the word 'Nosode' derives from the Greek word 'root-disease' and it has been exclaimed (by a Dr F.X. Mayr MD) that 'the gut is the root of the human being' (der Darm ist die Wurzel des Menschen) and that an unhealthy diet changes our genetic make-up within two generations; for example, if the grandfather suffered diabetes then his grandchildren have an increased risk to suffer from it, too.

It was only when Dr Bach accepted a position at the London Homœopathic Hospital in 1919, where he was given '**The Organon of the Rational Art of Healing**' first written and published in 1810 by Hahnemann in order to understand the philosophy of the Hospital, that he became interested in procedures of potentisation or dynamisation of these bowel bacteria. (**The Organon**, as it is now called for short, was the result of 20 years research by Hahnemann and right up to his death he tirelessly worked to improve it and published further editions. The sixth and last one, although finished in 1842 was not published until the early 1920s.)

Bach was most impressed with Hahnemann's writings and not only studied the disease causing bowel bacteria but worked out a '**mental portrait**' for each Nosode. The miasmatic theory given by Hahnemann led Bach to compare 'Psora' (which Hahnemann called the hundred headed hydra) with the **intestinal toxaemia**, resulting in the poisoning of the body from within.

He named the first seven groups of Bacilli as follows:

1. **Proteus – a polyvalent of several coli-bacteria:**
   Proteus vulgaris, inconstant, mirabilis, rettgeri and iliacus

2. **Dysentery – a composite of Dysenteriae bacilli**

3. **Morgan Bach – later subdivided (by Paterson) into:**
   Morgan Pure and Morgan Gaertner

4. **Faecalis Alkaligenes – Streptococcus faecalis**

5. **Coli Mutabile – Coli bacterium mutabile**

6. **Gaertner – Salmonella enteritidis**

7. **No. 7** (it is believed that he had run out of names)
   This was the 7th non-lactose fermenting bacillus observed in the laboratory

Other staff in the hospital were also impressed with Dr Bach's work, especially the Scottish physician **Dr John Paterson (1890-1955)** who continued the research in 1930 at the time when Dr Bach left London in his search of **seven herbs which would match the seven groups of bacteria.** Later Bach realised that more than just seven herbs were needed, thus we now have 36 of them.

Dr Paterson, with his wife Elizabeth, studied the bowel flora more deeply and during over 20 years of research examined more than 20,000 stool specimens. The conclusions of this extensive research were as follows:

◉ B. Coli or Colibac (medical name; Escherichia coli) is the **NON-LACTOSE** fermenting non-pathogenic bowel flora. Its general function is to break down chime in the gut but may undergo changes during disease conditions and may actually turn **pathogenic.** The disturbance of the fine balance in the bowel flora during disease is similar to those changes observed in the drug proving.

Dr Paterson gave us the two other Bowel Nosodes, which are included in my study with regards to the chakras:

SYCOTIC CO. Here again we have the 'co' for the composition of a 'gram negative diplococcic', meaning they stay together in pairs: The Diplococcic pneumonia and Neisseria gonorrhoea and/or Meningococcal meningitis that were found in the bowel. Therefore Paterson believed that this is directly related to the Sycotic Miasm. This Streptococcus faecal can be found in dairy or similar food products. It is amongst the most common disease causing bacteria in humans and is responsible for simple tonsillitis or scarlet fever, to cellulitis as well as more serious conditions like rheumatic fever. ('Gram' refers to staining them in the laboratory, in order to identify them.)

MORGAN-GAERTNER (he divided the Morgan group into Morgan Pure and Morgan Gaertner). The bacilli for Morgan Pure are Proteus morganii, while Morgan Gaertner includes Salmonella enteritidis and Proteus morganii.

One of the findings of Paterson and his wife was that every Bowel Nosode is affiliated to one or two of our big homœopathic polychrests. For example, when taking a case you may very clearly see Arsenicum Album emerging as your remedy of choice and you can immediately conclude that this patient will also do well on Dys-co.

All Bowel Nosodes should really end with Co. as it stands for **COMPOUND** and refers to the fact that they were all made up from the specific germs in each case. For example, **Morgan Co**. is the potentised vaccine made up from some hundreds of bacillus **Morgan**.

As early as 1880 another bacteriologist by the name Eberth succeeded in isolating and identifying the B.Typhosus – a non-lactose fermenting gram negative bacillus. Other disease causing bacteria later included the bacillary dysentery, paratyphoid and bacterial food poisoning followed quickly, such as the well known **Salmonella**.

These organisms present in the colon include not only bacilli such as *Escherichia coli*, which can cause acute gastroenteritis in infants, and *Entrerobacter aerogenes*, which includes Shigella causing Dysentery, but also organisms such as *cocci* of various types.

Organisms such as **gas gangrene bacilli** can cause serious disease in tissues of the colon, as well as ulceration and death of soft tissues giving off an unpleasant smell. When passed in the stool great masses of bacteria can cause epidemics of gangrene, as has been well documented during times of natural disasters or war. For example, the presence of Clostridium welchii or gas gangrene (the very virulent type of these bacteria) in the trenches of WWI with no proper sanitation <u>was lethal</u> to injured soldiers. Nowadays problems of gangrene have been overcome by penicillin, which was not available in the days of WWI. Other types of the Clostridium, such as Clostridium botulism, causes food poisoning, and Clostridium tetani, which can be found in soil, can result in tetanus or lockjaw, as it used to be called.

Although not included in my table of the Bowel Nosodes I would like to point out that **Mutabile (Bach)**, which is a **form of B.Coli**, can be **used in urinary infections and is closely related to Pulsatilla**. The other Bowel Nosode not listed in the table is **Faecalis (Bach)**, which is **akin to Sepia**.

Until 1925 when Dr E. Bach and Dr Charles Wheeler (1868-1946, born in Australia, studied Medicine in Leipzig, Germany and in London; he was another great Homœopath, being president of the Faculty of Homœopathy) published the book called 'Chronic diseases – A Working Hypothesis', no one had really taken any interest in 'non-lactose fermenting gram negative bacilli' and many thought that these were harmless. Of course the majority of the intestinal bacteria is perfectly normal and harmless and in fact performs a very useful function. If the intestinal mucosa is a healthy one then B.Coli is non-pathogenic. Only if changes in the **host** take place and upset the balance of the bio-chemistry will it become pathogenic. It modifies in order to survive: survival of the fittest! (Even bacteria lives by this fundamental rule of nature.)

An early attempt at using bowel material for medication came in the 17th Century when a German medical doctor by the name of Michael Ernst Ettmueller used pigs' stool to stop haemorrhaging, and horse manure as a remedy for 'hysteria'. The homœopathic Bowel Nosodes administered on lactose globules are a much 'cleaner and easier' way of addressing disease.

In the past there were always four reasons to give a Bowel Nosode listed:

1 Symptom-similarity.
2 When the apparently indicated remedy fails.
3 No remedy clearly indicated.
4 Several remedies acted but none cured.

I would like to add another reason:

5 **Relating to the chakras!**

Before introducing the chakras, however, we should first investigate the aura and our energy bodies.

Chapter FOUR

Introducing the Energy Bodies

Everything that has its origin in your consciousness is a form of ENERGY. Consciousness can be considered as having three aspects: the conscious, the subconscious or unconscious, and the super-conscious. Consciousness *is* **LIFE ENERGY, or creative force:** Hahnemann called it the **VITAL FORCE.**

The natural state of consciousness is BALANCE. Healing is the return to your natural state of balance and wholeness. Many levels of healing need to be addressed when no longer 'in balance':

PHYSICAL

EMOTIONAL

MENTAL

SPIRITUAL

For millions of years we fulfilled the plan of the GOD self and there was harmony and peace – 'as above, so below'. We now call this time **'Paradise'** or the 'Garden of Eden'. However, 'free will' – 'eating from the tree of good/bad', spoiled things. **The ego wanted to know what 'BAD' was!** (However, everything has a place in this grand plan and only here on planet EARTH can we learn from our past and present mistakes.)

Bad created 'worse' and the rest is **HIS-STORY** (GOD'S story is our story).

Hahnemann aptly named his 'Art of Healing' 'Homœopathy', a copulation meaning:

HOMO = Man
EO = Latin for go or flow, to be changed to, or to be in the place of
PATHY = suffering

These wonderful and wise words demonstrated that once in the 'flesh' and no longer in 'Spirit', man has changed place from being 'whole', where the energies flows freely and unrestricted, to a place of suffering: From this situation on the path of suffering man finds himself in need of remedies to reverse the suffering or lessen the burden.

We must **HEAL THE PAST**; one of the reasons why we often take so long during a first consultation is that we ask the new patient about the medical history of the family, as well as their own. 'Insults from the past' that result from vaccinations, physical/verbal abuse, traumas, operations, medication, or even daily stress, each create mental/emotional 'layers' that can build up and, like an 'onion', must be peeled back to the core. For example, mental/emotional mistreatment can arise from being called 'names' by other children at school (sadly not uncommon these days, with bullying currently so much talked about). This could bring about 'delusions', such as feeling 'insulted' or 'persecuted', which may result in a self-created loneliness! The questions a homœopath has to ask during a consultation are almost too numerous to mention.

We have to learn to **LIVE IN THE NOW** and **CREATE THE FUTURE**! With much less baggage from the past – which we can address with remedies – life will be a happier one!

Suffering also means 'less light inside as well as around the body' – **LIGHT is Energy**! Where there is light no darkness can exist!

Not so long ago a German Professor by the name of **Popp** – or rather one of his inspired students for his PhD – developed a 'light detecting' instrument able to detect that the 'light' in cancer patients **'was going out'**. I would like here to briefly digress on the subject of this is relatively recent research (within the last 30 years) that in places reads like a witch hunt:

Fritz-Albert POPP, born in 1938 in Germany, studied physics in Wurzburg at the same University where Wilhelm Roentgen accidentally 'stumbled' across x-rays, the electromagnetic (EM) frequency that could produce images of the human body. After his studies he joined the University of Marburg to teach radiology, during which time he believed that he had found the cure for cancer.

In his chosen profession he was a real 'whiz-kid' and had been awarded a PhD in 'theoretical science' in the record time of 2 years (instead of the usual 5). By the age of 33 he was working with carcinogens and 'weak' light of 380 nanometres (nm) – which is within the range of ultra violet rays. Note that visible violet light has a range from 380 to 410 nm! Carcinogens reacted only to the light of these specific wavelengths.

Prof. Popp noticed that 'photo-repair' in cells works most efficiently at 380 nm. This is the same wavelength that carcinogenic compounds would react to and scramble the cells in the first place – causing cancer. He felt that this was almost as if NATURE was 'perfect', having the answer to the problem it caused in the first place. However, when presenting his research during an eight day conference in 1970 at the German Cancer Research Centre in Heidelberg in front of the World's leading specialists, they thought he was 'cracking some kind of joke'! Light in the body? Photo-repair? Only one researcher from the Madame Curie Institute in Paris was impressed and asked him to join her at the Institute. Unfortunately she died of cancer herself before he could do so.

How could he prove he was right? The answer was a student by the name of Bernard Ruth, who had asked Professor Popp to supervise his PhD thesis. Prof. Popp agreed, saying "sure, if you can show me that there is light in the body". Ruth thought that this was a crazy suggestion. Popp's response was: "Okay, then show me that there is NO light in the body and you will get your PhD". As a brilliant physicist within 2 years he produced an instrument resembling an x-ray detector, which was able to count light, photon by photon.

In 1976 they started testing it. The first subject was a humble cucumber, which they found emitted photons but thought that the light-emissions detected might have been due to Chlorophyll producing – 'light'. So they tried potatoes instead, grown in total darkness. To their surprise the light emission reading was even higher. They called this emitted light **'BIOPHOTON EMISSIONS'**. The question was, where were these photons coming from?

To cut a long story short – it comes from the DNA. Other researchers in different countries had been experimenting with low currency since the 1920s, but before the 'Popp light machine' no equipment had been sensitive enough to measure the 'radiation' theory of DNA.

Here are some of Popp's finding: animals and plants that were tested emitted 100 photons per square centimetre per second (photons cm^{-2} s^{-1}) – at wavelengths between 200 and 800 nm (the visible part of EM spectrum = the colours), whereas humans only emitted 10 photons cm^{-2} s^{-1} at the frequency. To maintain a delicate equilibrium in the body it should not be bombarded with too much light, since the living 'systems' would reject the excess. (Think of skin cancer from too much sunbathing!)

They also discovered that the emission of these photons followed a regular biological rhythm at 7, 14, 32, 80 and 270 days, as well as diurnal (night and day) and other biological rhythms (moon cycle – menstrual cycle).

In cancer patients these natural periodic rhythms Popp found were not present. The lines of internal communication seemed scrambled; they had lost their connection with the world. In effect, **their light was going out.** In contrast, the opposite seemed to be the case with multiple sclerosis (MS) patients – they seemed to have 'too much light', creating chaos; they were 'drowning in light'.

When testing chicken eggs he found that the photons emanating from 'free range' eggs were far more coherent than those from 'battery eggs'. The same was true of other food, too. Healthier food had the lowest and more coherent intensity of light. Any disturbance in the system would increase the production of photons, leading to the conclusion that when we are ill our waves are out of synchronisation.

When publishing his findings in Germany, fellow scientists believed he had gone 'too far'. In 1980, when his contract at the University of Marburg came up for renewal, they asked him to leave. Two days before the end of term they 'raided' his laboratory and wanted to confiscate his equipment. Thankfully, Popp had been 'tipped off' and managed to hide it in one of his students' cellar. (A witch-hunt in the 20th Century?)

The university had literally made him 'redundant', owing him about 40,000 DM (the equivalent of about £9,000 at the time) but refusing to pay. He had to take the University to court and eventually got his pay due, but his career was in ruins and no university in Germany would offer him a post. With a young family (3 children) to support he had to find employment and the only company to offer him a job was Roedler – a homœopathic pharmacy. Here he worked for the next two years, and of course they actually believed in the theory.

When asked by a fellow Professor Walter Nagl from Kaiserslautern to work with him, the University of this town could not 'agree' with his ideas. Finally he did find employment in the research field again, in the Technology Centre in Kaiserslautern, which the government sponsored for special research.

At last other scientists from around the world took note of his research and began to agree with him, and soon after job offers for a professorship began to come in. After nearly twenty years of being the 'outsider', he was finally in demand.

During that time he had searched for substances to successfully support the treatment of cancer. The one he found most successful was MISTLETOE. One example is the case of a 30 year old woman with terminal breast and vaginal cancer: In this particular case it was with the doctor's permission that the woman was given just this herb, after findings that mistletoe extract had worked well on the cancer cells in the laboratory. After one year of therapy her 'light' was properly restored. In Homœopathy we know mistletoe as 'Viscum Album', while in anthroposophical medicine it is called 'Iscador', which the German anthroposophist Rudolf Steiner (1861-1925) suggested as a remedy for cancer patients.

Quantum and nuclear physics will provide some of the answers that we are looking for. With smaller and smaller particles being discovered the probabilities are endless. Quantum physics also tells us that these fundamental particles can communicate with one another in an 'energetic way' **over any distance instantaneously**; this is the **'spooky action at a distance'** phenomenon that **Albert Einstein** famously distrusted. By 1982, however, physicists had verified the possibility of this quantum entanglement. Einstein's famous equation helps us to understand some of what Popp was seeing:

$$E = mc^2 \text{ (energy is proportional to mass).}$$

This equation demonstrated that energy and mass are equivalent. The two previously thought-of separate physical entities of energy and mass had merged into one; all physical matter could now be described in terms of its energy – matter is the physical manifestation of ENERGY!

The implications of this equation were profound: all matter in the universe, regardless of size, mass and density, from the smallest grain of sand on the beach to the densest star in space, everything is made up of energy. At the quantum level all matter is essentially a collection of electrical charges that hold an object together and interact with external electromagnetic and other energetic fields; the energy of our physical bodies are equally interacting with those of others, with the energies of all surrounding matter (animals, plants, trees, rocks etc.), and with the background energetic fields.

In her fascinating book 'The Field', Lynne McTaggart describes what is known as the Zero Point Field. This **FIELD** is an ocean of microscopic vibrations that appear to connect everything in the universe; it gives the concept that we are no longer separate entities, or indeed separated with our surroundings, rather we are all interrelated and always interacting with everything else at an energetic level. It may be considered similar to the idea of the FORCE in the Star Wars films; 'may the force be with you'! This **pulsating energy field** drives our **'central engine'** and is a **'blue-print'** of all the memories of all our lives, and can help us to finally accept the truth that we have been here (have lived) before and will come back many more times in order to 'graduate' from this school of life.

The vastness of this field is immense. According to the book the total energy of the Zero Point Field exceeds all energy matter by the factor of 10^{40}, or 1 followed by 40 zeros. Such a huge value is almost incomprehensible although from a homœopathic point of view it is a familiar factor, albeit on the other end of the scale: rather than an expansion to such immeasurable quantities homœopathy deals with dilution to infinitesimal values. A remedy of potency 30 c, for example, is one that has been diluted by 1 in 10^{30}, which is the equivalent of saying that of the original substance that has been potentised only 1 part in 1 followed by 30 zeros remains.

Coming back from this digression to topic of cancer and the reduced amount of light in the body, the illness of cancer is excellently described by Louise Hay in her book 'HEAL YOUR BODY': 'Deep hurt. Longstanding resentment. Deep secrets or grief eating away at the self.' Carrying hatred and asking oneself: 'What's the use?' Well, HATE is the opposite of LOVE.

Love is the answer. Love yourself and your neighbour, without the EGO getting in the way. The more love and compassion there is the more light we have within our Aura and the more we will **'glow'** – resulting in a greater healing taking place. One could say it is a bit like falling in LOVE, when we radiate 'love' and thus glow, or when looking at the love of a mother to her newborn baby; I am sure that if we could see the Aura we would see a lot of lovely soft PINK emanating from the baby.

Some of these lights/energies seen in colours can be photographed with Kirlian photography, which is a procedure in which the various colours surrounding the body can be captured and reproduced on paper. The technique is named after the Russian electronic engineer Semjon Kirlian, who developed this high frequency photographic technique with his wife Walentina in the middle of the last century (1939-1958). Usually the first 30cm of the Aura around the body is captured, while the whole AURA expands much further depending on the 'energy' of that person – up to 350cm from the body. Kirlian photography has been improved with the aid of computers.

Apart from a photograph of the whole aura, the electromagnetic energy of parts of the body may also be photographed, where the meridians of the Qui energy are present.

For example, the hands or feet may be captured where the Qui energy produces a corona around the fingertips or toes. These coronas can be used as a diagnostic tool, rather like the iris, to indicate congestion or degeneration, or inflammation in certain organs or systems, such as the lymphatic system; all can be seen and interpreted by a skilled diagnostician.

Every living organism has an AURA and in earlier days these were depicted in paintings as halos around the heads of saintly people. However, we all have an aura (even if we are not saints) and some people, especially children, are often able to see them. When my daughter was about eleven years old she surprised me one day, when she saw a book about Auras on my desk and asked: "Mummy, what is an Aura?" When I explained that it is the energy field around the body, which we cannot see, yet is still there and represents the kind of electro-magnetic halo, she said: "Oh is that what I can see!" "You can see that?" was my response, and "lucky you, I wish I could". I then asked her if she could tell the colours of my aura on that day, as of course it can change with the moods we are in and the health that we are 'displaying' at the time. Presently she started concentrating and came up with 'mainly green' at the time, if I remember rightly. Another time when my sister was very poorly, my daughter confirmed that she could see only a kind of 'grey' around the body, with no real colours or vibrancy!

Homœopathic remedies, too, have an aura and I have seen books in Germany showing the different remedies with different lights around them, with different potencies displaying varying strengths of the remedies by more intense colouring.

Incorporating Colours and Vibrations as Remedies

Colours, of course, have different **frequencies**. Their **wavelengths** are measured in nanometres (nm) in the visible spectrum and, starting with red, are as follows:

Red	625-700 nm
Orange	595-625 nm
Yellow	570-595 nm
Green	495-570 nm
Blue	440-495 nm
Indigo	410-440 nm
Violet	380-410 nm

The above seven colours are connected to the 7 major chakras.

These colours are made into homœopathic remedies. In the book 'Homeopathic Colour remedies' Ambika Wauters gives us a wonderful overview of these 'colour' remedies, offering us a better understanding not just of the colours, but also of their usage and when it is appropriate to choose a particular colour remedy. Nowadays the frequencies of these colours may be measured with modern instruments, but before this was possible the 'Spirit' of the colours was known: Therefore these colours of the prism can help us in our daily meditation to learn the qualities and virtues they represent.

The Spirit of the colour RED is known as the 'Spirit of Life'.
RED is tied to life. It is also the colour of love, as well as of the blood.
Red is connected to the BASE chakra.

The Spirit of the colour ORANGE is called the 'Spirit of Sainthood'.
ORANGE improves your health and urges you on to perfection.
Orange is connected to the SACRAL Chakra.

The Spirit of the colour of YELLOW is the 'Spirit of Wisdom'.
YELLOW inspires us to meditate and reflect, to understand, to be reasonable and careful.
Yellow is connected to the SOLAR PLEXUS.

The Spirit of the colour GREEN is the 'Spirit of Eternity and Evolution'.
GREEN is linked to growth and expansion, richness and recourse.
They say green is the colour of hope, because it helps man to evolve.
Green is connected to the HEART chakra.

The Spirit of the colour BLUE is the 'Spirit of Truth'.
BLUE is tied to religion, to peace and music.
Blue develops a feeling for music, calms the nervous system,
heals the lungs and acts favourably on the eyes, which are linked to truth.
Blue is connected to the THROAT Chakra.

The Spirit of the colour INDIGO is the 'Spirit of Force'.
INDIGO is the colour for Royalty. Royalty with a vision!
Indigo is connected to the THIRD EYE.

The Spirit of VIOLET is the 'Spirit of the divine Supreme Power'.
VIOLET stands for Spiritual Love and Sacrifice.
Violet is a very powerful colour, it protects and enables man to
leave his body and explore other worlds.
It permits him to understand the love of GOD.
The violet light will help to set us free, its vibration is that much higher and
thus spins that much faster, and of course it is associated the CROWN Chakra.

The PHYSICAL BODY – Energy Body No. 1

The CHAKRAS are connected to our more SUBTLE BODIES, each taking time after birth to 'develop', just like the body does. Each subtle body takes seven years to develop and thus it takes 28 years to manifest the four lower bodies; this is usually the time when we have fully 'grown up' into adulthood and should be able to leave home, give or take a year or two. If the four lower subtle bodies are in harmony and at peace, filled with love and joy, the process of inner healing and glowing will begin.

William Wordsworth said: 'Our birth, but a sleep, a forgetting.
                             This process of divine transformation,
                             is part of our awakening.
                             Awakening to this still point in each of us.
                             This still point is untouched by time.
                             This is our divine point of entrance into timeless eternity.'

Great Avatars – great Souls and teachers like **Jesus, Buddha, and Krishna** – have visited the earth to remind us of who we are and to help us to '**see the light again**'.

Recently, I was given a channelling from Merlin (who was a prophet, but who is more well-known as the mythical wizard to the legendary ruler of Britain, King Arthur), in which it said: 'You are Masters – that you may not believe, or know it of yourselves, does not alter the truth of it, only your experience of it'. I guess we have to try harder to truly understand ourselves and the power we hold within.

Thoughts are like Magnets – if you are friendly and cheerful you will invite 'friendliness' into your life. On the other hand if you curse all the time, the curses will haunt you. Like the Bible teaches us, 'what you sow, you will harvest here'! (This is Karma). We could also call it an **ECHO**: Whatever you shout will come back to you, often several times, like an echo! This could be for good, as well as for bad! This is one of the reasons why as parents we need to teach our children the right morals, in order for them to learn about KARMA or the ECHO, whichever word you prefer.

Let us take a closer look at our **THOUGHTS, WORDS and DEEDS.** Before I come to discussing the **Emotional Body** I feel I need to say a little more about the **Physical Body**, which is our vehicle in this life, in this incarnation. We should treat this body like a temple, keeping it pure and clean, which can assist the ascension. One way of achieving this is by fasting and drinking plenty of pure water to detoxify the body. I personally feel that the Bowel Nosodes play an important part in helping this internal cleaning, as without purification we have putrefaction. For a long and happy life it is vital to keep the body free of toxins, in this case internal ones, which are produced by <u>fermentation in the gut.</u> This fermentation has a negative influence on the 'Personality'. Let me give a brief explanation of what is meant by the Personality.

Without the ETHERIC FIELD, which is an exact copy of the physical body with all the organs and systems in place, we could not function at all. At the time of death when the ENERGY withdraws we become just a shell; **no personality** and **no individuality** are noticed by those watching a dying person. The last breath is the final withdrawing of the soul back to spirit, taking with it the personality we once were; like a light bulb when the electricity is switched off, there is no 'spark' left. This electricity animated us and gave the impulse to the nervous system. Broadly speaking, the **personality** belongs to the three lower chakras, while **individuality** is part of the higher self and belongs to the upper chakras. The heart in the middle will connect the two.

The individuality is located in the body above the diaphragm, centred on the heart, with the lung and the brain being part of it. The more we cultivate this energy of the individual the more 'radiant' we become and the more charming we are perceived by others. We start to have trust not just in ourselves but in the Universe, too. Then, rather than 'my will be done', we can accept that 'thy will be done' and life flows a lot easier as it is us who 'provide' the obstacles out of fear. (Fear, remember, is the Base Chakra).

The energy of the heart should in its wisdom, be sharing, dividing and spreading happiness. The heart as you will see is represented by the SUN, which governs our lives here on earth. If we spell it slightly differently it becomes the 'SON'. In the Christian religion the 'son of God' was represented by Christ. However, long before Christianity arrived a mere two thousand years ago (a very short time in the history of mankind) other religions also spoke of the return of the 'SUN/SON'! This return of the SUN was celebrated with the festival of the Winter Solstice (on 21st December), now the time of Christmas! Other pre-Christian festivals such as the Spring or Autumn Equinoxes (on 21st March and 21st September, respectively) are not quite so prominently marked in the Christian calendar. Even though Easter is celebrated very close to the Spring Equinox, the date corresponds to the first full moon after the Spring Equinox, which is one reason why the dates of Easter vary from year to year.

Finally, the Summer Solstice, or Midsummer's night (on 21st June), was also a time of great celebration (and for some people it still is). Traditionally, Midsummer's night was celebrated from the 20th, 21st and 22nd of June, while the 23rd and 24th are still public holidays in some Continental countries, representing Saint John's Eve and Saint John's day and celebrating the feast of St. John the Baptist, when a person was supposed to discover their true love. The true love awaiting discovery does not only represent finding a partner but could also be discovering true love of oneself; indeed many people do not know even how to respect and love themselves in a non-selfish way, leave alone loving their neighbours! If this LOVE is merely for **personal gain** then we have dropped **again** into the lower realms of the **Personality**, instead of involving the heart chakra (even the word a-gain says you want to 'gain'), which seldom brings joy, as it is restricting and limiting. True love comes through wisdom of the **Individual**. Coming back to the CHRIST born to us as the son of God, we must realise that we all have this Christ-energy in us and when moving into the heart chakra we live by the principles of compassion and 'love thy neighbour', as given as one of the commandments.

The intellect can be a blessing as well as a curse. Unfortunately, the intellect wants to play the 'power game', which causes so much tragedy in the world: Not just today, it always has! The intellect can be full of pride, suspicion, scorn and criticism. When nobody will acknowledge the 'intellect' and when obstacles are put in its way, it will be full of hate and rage. This hate and rage becomes a poison to that personality and others around them, in turn creating 'hell on Earth'. On the other hand our discriminating intellect enables us to make informed decisions and to consider our actions before choosing right from wrong, leaving nothing to regret later. This will include the 'spoken word', since this audible vibration called 'speech' is unique to the human kingdom and can be used to hurt others, as well as nurture and heal!

Coming back to the chakras, as far as I am aware, these can be attributed to a gender, with each relating to either masculine or feminine principles. Starting at the bottom the base chakra has a male principle, whilst the next chakra is the sacral and is 'Female', and the subsequent Solar Plexus is again 'Male'. Continuing, the heart chakra above is feminine. These attributions, however, should not be regarded as either good or bad as we need both energies. For example, without the male energy, which is very much a 'driving force', we would not be as far advanced in our technology, since men in their search and research need everything in black and white. The female principles follow the intuition more, giving us much greater 'insight' to things and how people work. Let us say that these energies very much complement each other.

A word about animals; in Homœopathy the remedies are **never tested** on animals. To gain an understanding of a particular substance (herb, mineral, metal, etc.) that should be made into a remedy we carry out what is known as a **'proving'**. This is the collection and correlations of symptoms – physical, as well as mental/emotional – provided by a group of volunteers who take a particular **remedy** in a variety of potencies over either days or weeks. They report back on their experiences with this remedy and with this provide the 'proving picture'. With this remedy picture we can therefore also treat animals very successfully according to their symptoms. By comparison, allopathic medicine tested on animals (who are guided by a group soul) will always have similar results, which can be either positive or negative depending of what the testing laboratory has tried to achieve. The laboratory testers can only observe physical symptoms that the medication induces in the animal, but not the emotions it may cause. Since the animals cannot describe these emotional effects it will be left to chance what 'mind-altering' conditions may come as a side-effect when the drug is later taken by humans. In the news not so long ago there was a story about a number of people who tried to commit suicide after taking a certain drug for a number of weeks or months, which could have been due to this effect! Another case springs to mind where a father of two boys diagnosed with attention deficit disorder (ADD) told me that he certainly did not agree with the medication prescribed for his children after he had tested it on himself and felt 'high' for hours, as though he had been doped with LSD. As humans have feelings and thoughts, which are constantly changing, a different approach to true healing is needed.

If the owner of a pet can describe the character of the animal the choice of a remedy can be made in the same way that one would choose a remedy for a small child not able to express itself; in this case, the mother/father provides the symptoms and likes and dislikes etc. of the child, and the homœopath observes the child's expressions, skin colouring and the interaction with the parent present, to give clues of the most suitable remedies.

Other animals that are not house pets, such as those on a farm for example, can be treated by disease names and symptoms accordingly, even if the particular character of the animal is not well-known. The closer the animal lives in the proximity of humans, the greater it will develop on a soul level and learn behaviour patterns, even if it returns in its next life/lives as an animal. This is not to belittle the animal in any way; there are lots of stories in which animals have saved lives, even sacrificing their own life in the process. The love and devotion they can show to their 'owner' is beyond duty, so to speak. Just as we can teach animals 'a few tricks', we can learn a lot from them and some therapies now involve animals to teach us 'real values'.

So much about our physical body, which we share with all living creatures: The next in the Aura is the 'Emotional Body'. However, before we move onto the next one a final word about the physical body and the first aura, which by some philosophers is called our 'etheric skin', being the shell immediately next to the body and associated with the 'Base Chakra'. The etheric skin is no more than 10cm wide and easily 'sensed' by everyone: If you hold your hands apart – about 20cm – you can sense or feel a kind of magnetic pull or a tingling in your hands, like holding a cotton wool ball between the hands. I have never come across anyone who does not feel anything, unless of course they do not 'want' to feel anything, as it frightens and is too 'spooky' for them (fear = base chakra). I cannot press this point enough, as it is the fear that leads to inertia and no flow; and 'no flow' **leads to disease, which is located in this energetic skin**, allied to the colour RED with a wavelength of 625-700 nm. As a remedy this colour can be used to help people make the 'next move in life'.

The EMOTIONAL BODY – Energy Body No. 2

The Emotional Body was created like a 'cradle' for the rest of the four lower bodies, so we should try to make it a 'Happy Cradle.'

The Emotional Body – or emotional intelligence, i.e. the feelings – is one of the most difficult to master. Like Planet Earth, 80% of the human body is water and here all present feelings, as well as karmic feelings, are locked in. **Until we have mastered these we need to re-incarnate.** (Another scary thought, I guess.)

The Emotional Body can also be called the **'Desire Body'** and so we have to be careful **'what we wish for!'** (We have all heard the saying: 'Be careful what you ask for'!) In the Lord's Prayer this is addressed in the line: "lead us not into temptation". Regular recitation of this will help to clear the aura of the desire body; but more about that at the end of the book. This is not to say that the Lord's Prayer of the Christians is the only way that this can be done. It can also be achieved in many other ways, with chants, or other prayers, or through workshops that teach us to look within.

Recently I listened to a lecture by Brandon Bays introducing her **Journey Work**. The title of the lecture was **'Emotions: The gateway to Freedom'**. I could not agree more with her, that if we can be masters of our emotions then we will have a 'ticket' to the 'gateway of freedom'. She told us about her JOURNEY, her own health problem and how

guilty she felt all the time when falling ill and not being able to 'serve her clients all the time', no matter what time of day or night! From the homœopathic point of view it is no wonder that she developed a tumour, which meant she had to stop and reflect on what she was doing and completely change her routine. Now she goes around the world to lecture people on how to overcome their EMOTIONS. (This is one reason why I believe we need the higher potencies in Homœopathy; this, too, will be discussed in the conclusion.)

In her book **'Heal your body'** Louise Hay links the emotions to disease. In the book's introduction she describes how she was diagnosed with cancer of the vagina, which was linked to the fact that she was raped when only five years old and was a 'battered' child. Until her medical diagnosis was in black and white she had not realised **'how much deep resentment she had harboured'**. Within six months she cleansed her body and mind, and more importantly changed her 'thought patterns'. Having done all of that, the miracle happened and she got the all 'clear' from the doctors.

It sounds so simple, but to change **'negative'** thought patterns into **'positive'** ones is a hard learning experience. To 'let go' can be the hardest lesson we have to come across. (Look at the word 'a-cross': If we do not manage to let go we carry the 'cross' forever, until we have a (nervous) 'breakdown' of some sort. This can be physical or mental.) Remedies can work wonders before this point is reached, preventing the worst scenario being played out in our 'live-show', in which we play the **major part**. If only we could get back the feelings of joy and **not to hold grudges!** Enthusiasm for your life is the key; a job we love, a new hobby, anything that can lift you to new heights and give you back the zest for life. The emotions to focus on here, naming just a few, include:

Positive: LOVE, PEACE, TRUST, HAPPINESS, JOY, ENTHUSIAM.

However, should we 'prefer' to stay in the negative emotions they will drag us down and bring 'dis-ease'. **Negative** emotions are: **FEAR, ANXIETY, ANGER, HATE, SADNESS, and GUILT de-motivating oneself.**

This **Desire** or **Emotional body** 'grows', manifesting itself from the age of seven to fourteen; most parents know how demanding budding teenagers can be in their desires …. 'I want, I want, I want'… is expressing their 'Desire body' and testing it out on the parents. With the onset of puberty, hormones arrive on the stage in this 'Play of Life' and an interest in the opposite sex starts growing daily! It is not an easy time for the teenagers, but also not for the parents, who constantly have to enforce their boundaries. Without boundaries these teenager can behave like 'wild horses', being difficult to catch and leash again. (The metal mercury as a remedy springs to mind here; 'catch them while you can', stopping the chaos before it develops).

From a homœopathic point of view we have an endless list of remedies to help with temper tantrums, not just of very young children but also for the hormonally 'imbalanced' teenagers that seem to think they 'know it all'! They often think that they are old enough to conduct their lives, yet use foul language and 'spit'. This dirty habit can be wonderfully addressed with remedies, like Mercury, Nit-ac. or Lyss. for 'spasmodic spitting'.

Nit-ac. could also be used if they 'burn out' from too many late nights, either due to pleasure or from studying for vital examinations and therefore not getting enough sleep. (Holding grudges about parental control can be another reason to give this remedy, when they become to 'prickly' to handle.) The sex drive very often needs to be calmed down in order to avoid a teenage pregnancy, which in England is particularly prevalent, having the highest teenage pregnancy rate in Europe; and that in spite of free contraceptives.

From experience I know that if the children have **never** had Homœopathy before it is very hard to begin giving them remedies in their teenage years. Teenagers rebel, especially if their mother or father wants them to take something to address their 'super-ego'. I always advise parents to start treatment long before puberty to avoid such 'naughty' teenagers, as a tendency of bad behaviour shows up a long time before puberty anyway. This can save the parents from the 'nightmares' shown daily on television, when situations with tearaway children often get out of hand.

In an ideal situation children should grow up having Homœopathic treatment; having had help with their little problems before they become 'big problems'. In Germany we have a saying: 'little children are little problem, big children are big problems'! Avoiding the whole scenario of unruly teenagers with remedies could make the teenage years a very joyous time for the parents.

As a mother of three, I certainly loved the independence the children were gaining, the wonderful conversations we started having with them, allowing them to express their points of view as a very valid one and thus creating great discussions rather then rows.

The Emotional body helps to create positive interpersonal relationships. It should therefore be able to recognise feelings and handle them appropriately, managing emotions to prove social competence and skills. This ability to recognise one's own emotions as well as those of others is part of self-awareness, as is the ability to help others process their emotions, for example bereavement, the loss of a job, or other bad news. Not all news has to be bad of course; some people are unable to handle good news, especially when their emotional body is too unstable and they are literally 'all over the place'. In relation to remedies a lack of emotional control can be helped by Carcinosin, Medorrhinum and Tuberculinum as miasmatic ones, plus Anacardium, Hyoscyamus, Tarantula and Veratrum Album, as expected these are in the same rubric. Again help is at hand in the form of Homœopathy.

Like the Sacral Chakra the 'Emotional Body' is related to the colour ORANGE and its wavelength of 595-625 nm. During the proving of this colour as a remedy by Ambika Wauters a sense of well-being and joy was expressed: This is how we *should* experience life and this colour can give us back the vitality that was lacking previously.

The MENTAL BODY – Energy Body No. 3

Having gone full swing into puberty the next hurdle needs to be taken. Now is the time, after age fourteen, to nurture the unfolding of the **Mental Body**, which is capable of creating original thought patterns. This takes place until the age of twenty-one, the time when we are 'supposed' to be fully fledged adults.

With more and more children now going into higher education we are actually giving them more time to 'grow'. The **Ego** is now moving into the **Mental Body**, helping these adolescents to shape their own futures and destinies. Thus further education is in my mind a very positive development, as previous generations were forced into early labour and consequently were not able to mature to an extent that they could have done if the need to earn money had not been so great: No time to think or study, only time to work. This is not to say that working early in life is a bad thing. Indeed training in a well-loved job can improve a person's mental abilities and positive views on life and fosters the ego, which in turn wants to achieve great things.

The **Ego** is in the **blood** and without the warm blood in the body the ego cannot express itself. The German poet Goethe knew about this, and in his play *Faust* he portrays the struggle of the higher and lower nature of man. Dr Faust makes a pact with the devil in the guise of Mephistopheles whereby he signs over his soul, using his blood as ink, for 'worldly reason', i.e. material gain and fame (the lower nature). The struggle of the higher self to evolve is condemned if the blood is too toxic, leading us astray to follow every pleasure and temptation coming our way. Mephistopheles says 'Blood is a most peculiar essence' and he knows that whoever owns the blood also 'has the man' hence he has power over Faust.

Blood on the energetic level is also very much associated with the metal iron (as will be discussed in chapter 5) and on the alchemic quest to turn lead into gold we have arrived at this metal. Iron also stands for 'power' and by 1000 BC the Iron Age was established, without which the industrial revolution could not have taken place. The saying 'strike while the iron is hot' means that one should act promptly when an opportunity arises. In people whose blood is 'weak' this enthusiasm to make progress will be lacking. Thus we can see that even from this metaphor, where iron needs to be shaped while it is hot, we can understand that a person deficient of iron in the blood is 'cold and stiff' and their 'fire element' is lacking. It also proves the point how vital it is that a young person should not suffer from anaemia, which causes constant tiredness at a time when the Mental Body is beginning to form and should create a strong energetic 'shield' around the body.

The Mental Body holds all of our thoughts via colours, tunes (musical notes) and form! Here we 'create' everything; we are true creators! When we die we take all of these 'creations' with us into the next world. This is a similar concept to that of the 'cellular memory' of the body in which, for example, a fatal injury of a previous lifetime may manifest itself in the present lifetime as a scar or health problem at the site of injury. Similarly we can consider the energy of our creations and knowledge analogous to the chip of a computer; we may write programmes and continuously develop and improve them to increase the chip's function and ability to perform more complex operations. These creations that are carried with us on the mental plane may often explain the special abilities of child prodigies. The young Mozart, for example, could play the instruments so well because he had played and possibly composed music in a previous life. Therefore for him it was literally 'child's play' as he had practised it many times before. This carrying over of creations, however, may only be desirable if we have created positively. The thought of all our negative creations also 'going with us' is a very scary thought, would you not agree? (Just like the feeling and the emotions of the 'desire body').

As thoughts are like magnets, we can also learn to 'tune' into other peoples thoughts and ideas; we pick them up and we call it 'telepathy'. We all know the sudden 'impression' we get that we need to phone a particular person and when acting on it the person might say: 'I was just about to call you, too', or something similar. There is no difference if the person lives in the same town or 'abroad'. Distance does not matter here!

The **Mental Body** can also be called the **'Mind'**, which we associate with the brain, yet has nothing to do with the intellect. The **Solar Plexus** is the seat of it, where the intestines are situated, and our 'second brain'. Here we get what we call 'our gut feelings' and often act on them rather more than on our analytical skills. A combination of the two, however, would be desirable.

I read somewhere that we think about **60,000** thoughts each day! Now if **95% are the same thoughts as the day before** then the organs will automatically be the same. Imagine now if only one quarter of those thoughts are negative; you have produced 15,000 'creations' that are detrimental to your health! **However, if we can change our thought pattern we can heal ourselves**. (Here we are back to our emotions, from the last chapter.) **Love, joy and laughter** are the best ingredients for new organs, which are constantly regenerated. The liver, for example, takes only six weeks to renew itself and at any one time 98% of the cells in the liver are new ones.

In comparison, skin takes only four weeks, and bones three and a half months. Since the bones are the slowest we can safely conclude that with nearly every season of the year we are a new person. Not only do we feel like a new person, we also feel different according to the seasons; therefore a good question for a homœopath to ask the patient would be: 'Which season do you like best?' This may be a very good way to discovering certain remedies that they might need. Only clients on too much medication have a problem here, as they are no longer 'in tune' with their body and do not know how they feel about the seasons. People living in rural areas may be closer and more in tune with nature than most city dwellers. They might feel more 'renewed' or may come back to life after the winter 'hibernation' when nature creates new energies all around; most people who live an urban life will most likely never be aware of this, at least not to its full extent. Yet there is hope for the future with the raising of energy and moving into the next dimensions. This is a time when we should all become more aware, not just of our physical body and paying attention to its needs, but also listening to our Spirit within. Like the Solar Plexus this 'Mental Body' is associated with the colour YELLOW and the wavelength of 570-595 nm. The colour remedy Yellow can help a person to 'feel better about themselves and boost their confidence' and like so many springtime flowers that have yellow blossoms, giving back the hope of good times ahead, the remedy will help to give a positive feeling and the outlook for a bright future.

The ASTRAL BODY – Energy Body No. 4

After the **Mental Body** comes the **Astral Body**, which is a little more difficult to describe as most of us only know the astral world as a place where 'lost souls' are stuck! This is true, if they do not realise at the time of death that they have passed over into the spirit world. A wonderful book that opened my mind to the **Astral** world was written and published in 1924 by the American psychiatrist Dr Carl A. Wickland M.D. and was called 'Thirty Years among the Dead!' Together with his wife, who acted as a 'medium' between the worlds, he helped his patients by freeing the 'entities' from the astral plane in their aura.

In his book Dr Wickland describes how an entity becomes attracted to a person's auric field. In the first instance it must be mentioned these entities did not realise that they were dead and no longer had a body after dying, as they felt very much 'alive'. (The spirit lives on and on). By attaching themselves to the person's aura (a person they took a liking to, or rather to their energetic field) gave them the feeling of having a 'body' through which they could express themselves. This could be one explanation of 'multiple personalities', where a person is talking to and being 'guided' by (or should I say 'mislead' by) someone that others cannot see. I am not saying this is always the case, but it could be one reason for odd behaviours and for refusing help, as they will be 'told' (by the attached entity) that nothing is wrong with them and that no treatment is needed. This of course is very detrimental for the poor 'victim' who will either display physical problems that the deceased person might have had, or who will literally go 'out of their mind' no longer in control of their destiny.

I would like to give one example here of a real physical problem of a patient described in Dr Wickland's book: The lady in question unexplainably became bedridden over night. During a séance with Mrs. Wickland it emerged that a man (unknown to the patient) had fallen off his horse and broken his neck in the physical body. In his mind, however, his astral body got up and he 'invited' himself into the aura of his 'friend', as he called the patient in this case. He was very happy that her husband looked after his 'friend', the poor lady, as this way **he** felt very much 'loved' and cared for (maybe for the first time in his last life). It was difficult to talk sense to him despite pointing out that he was very much interfering with his 'victim's' life and that she was unable to lead a normal life from the moment he had 'stepped in'. Finally, however, they managed to convince him to look for 'the light', only seen by those already in the 'after-life', and with gentle persuasion he vacated her aura. Immediately the miracle cure happened; the lady was no longer troubled by what seemed to her like having 'a broken neck and back'.

With the help of his wife the medium, Dr Wickland was able to 'talk' to these 'spirits'. The conversations are fascinating to read. Again and again these spirits do not want to believe that they are dead and in the realms of spirit and no longer in possession of their physical vehicle. It was no easy job telling them that they needed to return to 'the light'! This very often took some persuasion. Some, for example, would be happy to see loved ones, parents and grandparents, who had died before them and were waiting for them. These ancestors had been waiting patiently in order to move and assist them to reach higher dimensions. However, some got very frightened indeed, were very stubborn, and believed that they were seeing ghosts when passed relatives 'were standing nearby' waving and indicating to join them. Often it was only their mother that could entice them to unite with her, by the promise that she would take care and look after them, as she had always done.

When Dr Wickland was able to encourage these astral bodies to 'move on' his patients would have miraculous cures, as mentioned earlier. The book is full of case histories of his lifelong work with psychiatric patients. By writing them down, he hoped that more people would understand the 'subtle' world of spirit and how it works.

I can only recommend everybody to read his book, especially Homœopaths, as remedies spring to mind all the time when reading these cases, making it real fun to study. With HIGH potencies I feel we can help not only by strengthening the aura, but in my opinion these 'lost souls' will get the remedy too. Some of these could be remedies that they needed when they were still alive but that were not administered at that time.

To demonstrate this and how it works I would like to give an account of the case of a gentleman in Germany whose daughter died of a large tumour at the base of the spine about twelve months previous. When the first symptoms appeared, the daughter, who was in her early 30s, had tried not to worry her doting parents. Finally, when she was taken to hospital they were told a vague diagnosis of a cancerous growth of either the size of a football or a golf ball at the base of her spine! Now, there is a big difference between these two sizes and to this day the parents, very much to their distress, do not know how big it really was. It is almost unbelievable that in this day and age, with all the modern equipment available in hospitals that can reveal all, the parents would still not be told exactly how big the tumour was.

Chemotherapy and radiation treatment was given to 'kill' (or shrink) the tumour because an operation to remove it was out of the question. Unfortunately successive treatments weakened and eventually killed the patient, in fact rather more quickly than expected. Only three months or so transpired from the time I heard about this case until she died. Feeling dreadful from the toxic onslaught of the body, she suffered greatly in the last few weeks of her life. I am sure we all hear about such cases frequently and feel helpless 'watching' the event unfold.

About three or four months after the funeral I received a card from my sister's mother-in-law who had visited the family. In the card she wrote how much the father of the deceased daughter suffered from terrible back pain. So much in fact, that he could not sleep at night. He could only sit either in a hot bath to bring some relief, or alternatively he would sit in a deckchair in the sitting room to doze for 20 minutes or so, but otherwise moving about constantly. Lying in bed for any lengths of time would cause pain and he would therefore often restlessly pace up and down and was very anxious. As the pain was in the lower back – the very same place where his daughter's pain had been – he refused to see the doctor, blaming them of having killed his daughter with medication and not telling them the truth about her condition in the first place. (Maybe also fearing the worst for himself?)

Now, this was too much for me to ignore, even if I had not been asked for help. Being very loving grandparents they now had the daily task of looking after the two small children of their daughter while their son-in-law was at work. I just could not have him 'going down' as well. Consequently I put remedies together in 1M and 10M potencies, in particular Carcinosin, but others too to help him to 'let go' of the past events. Being very interested in 'spirituality', and knowing that he had a Homœopathic 'first aid kit' I was sure that he understood the concept that high potencies could offer more than the first aid kit he had in store. And indeed with the high potencies I had given him a true miracle happened: Within two days he could go to bed with much less pain and for the first time in 3 or 4 weeks could sleep again. Gradually, by the end of the first week of taking the remedies, he was almost pain free. As a bonus, after taking Carcinosin 10M he and his wife asked the father of the children to take care of the kids at the weekend so that they could have a 'child free' weekend, which they used to have a mini-holiday in the countryside. This was the first weekend since their daughter had passed over that they had to themselves, no longer being the 'victims' of the situation, which of course is very carcinogenic!

The next time I was visiting Germany he was keen to meet me and we discussed the remedies and potencies. I told him that by giving the high potency I was sure that I had also treated his deceased daughter as she had certainly not been 'cured' whilst still in the physical body and was possibly in limbo on the 'other side'. Of course in spirit the body cannot suffer like the physical body does, unless the memory is too strong to let go.

After her father had taken the remedies she could move on, lighter and brighter. Yet, the only way to get a dose of the remedy to her was to give it to her father, after he had expressed the same pains that she had suffered. He totally agreed with me, had tears in his eyes, and was so happy to have been able to possibly help her too, even if she was no longer in the physical body. He felt that if there was any chance to connect with her then the high potencies could achieve this. Of course, the Carcinosin helped him with the deep grief too, and being stuck in the 'feeling sorry state'. The parents also blamed themselves for having not done enough to prevent her 'catching' cancer. Yet, how do we prevent anyone from learning a life's lesson? However cruel these lessons seem to be at the time, do we really know what contracts were made by the soul before its incarnation? Was it not their choice to have, for example, a handicap in order to progress, not just for their own sake but for those around them too? With the aid of remedies we can lessen the burdens and reduce the suffering, but only in <u>agreement with the soul</u>.

The Astral Body is connected on the energetic plane to the 'Heart Chakra' and corresponds to the colour GREEN and its wavelength of 495-570 nm. It marks the boundary between the 'lower' physical vibrations and the higher bodies of the 'spiritual realms' on the subtle level. After death this Astral Body dissolves while the next one, the Etheric Body, which is part of the three 'upper bodies' remains eternally. **The Astral Body is also called the 'Spirit Body' in some books,** which brings me to the next Question: What is the SOUL and where is it?

The ETHERIC BODY and the SOUL – Energy Body No. 5

The physical world is where the 'dense' body functions. Fluids give us the minerals we need and solids give us our skeletal system structure, with our bones connected to the element 'earth'. Blood and the lymphatic system provide the fluids, with the element 'water' keeping the flow going. The nervous system acts like the fire, animating the body with great speed; thoughts can translate into action before they are even acknowledged in the mind. The element 'air' provides the breath we need to keep stay alive: without air we cannot survive. Thus the dense body can be concluded as comprising of the elements EARTH, WATER, FIRE and AIR. These belong to the four lower energy bodies.

The element ether is associated with one of the upper three energy bodies, namely the **Etheric Body**. This is an exact template or copy of the 'physical body' in the form of **Ether** – like a mirror. The word 'ether' derives from the Greek word 'aither', meaning upper air. It can be thought of as 'space' with never-ending sound as it says in the Bible: 'In the beginning was the word, and the word was God.'

The **Etheric Body** carries the energy blueprint of the DNA; part of the DNA is of course our inheritance from the 'family tree'. On the energetic level our accumulated experiences from different incarnations, which formed the various personalities assumed in each lifetime, are stored here. As Jesus said in the New Testament Math.25-40: 'Verily I say unto you inasmuch as ye has done it unto one of the least of these my brethren, ye have done it unto me'. This is not just in this life, but all previous ones as well.

Like an actor on the stage we put on a different mask and clothing for each individual lifetime, acting the part required in that particular play. In one role we might act a criminal, while in another a saint. As we have to experience every role in the rich 'tapestry of life' we experience a multitude of different lifetimes; sometimes as a man, other times as a woman; maybe poor, and yet in another lifetime rich. This tapestry is stored for us in the etheric world in what are termed the **Akashic records**. During meditation we are sometimes permitted to see parts of it where we can see the personalities that we have played, sometimes famous ones; other times just 'a face in the crowd' so to speak.

In order to change from just a **'Personality'** into an **'Individual'** not driven by material fame and gain, we have to search our 'Soul'. It can take a lot of 'soul-searching' to connect on this level, but the tools are there to be found in different places. In the bible it says: 'Knock and the door will be opened.' Once this door is open rejoice in achieving the task and the pleasure of being an instrument to nourish and guide others will be immense. (See Plato's cave parable in Chapter 5).

In the near future quantum physicists might provide the 'black and white' answers for the sceptics of how Homœopathy or other alternative healing methods work. Even without the answers, however, it does not mean that this 'life force' has ever left us 'standing in the cold'; it is always there as **'chi'** energy, whether we can explain it or not.

The Etheric Body is connected to the Throat Chakra, which is the chakra of 'expressing oneself'. The more unique an 'Individual' has become, the greater their expression and the wiser their words. Energy at this level, as with the other four primary chakras, manifests as subtle 'etheric' electromagnetic waves that envelope and permeates the 'Etheric Body'. When we consider the metal relating to the chakra which is connected to this 'energy body' we arrive at **Copper.** Copper is a wonderful conductor and therefore it is easy to understand that this chakra can easily pick up messages and relay them with great speed, as this is the place where 'intuitive hearing' has its seat.

It is in the Etheric body that we store our likes and dislikes, as well as our unique 'psychic scent', which can be detected by dogs; they are able to sniff out if you like or dislike them. These likes and dislikes can of course go back to early childhood memories, yet may go back to a past life too, with memories about events, either pleasant or unpleasant, not yet erased from this 'micro-chip' we seem to carry around with us from one life to the next. Modern technology demonstrates the ever increasing capacities of such tiny micro-chips capable of holding more and more information; I feel that we are currently getting better equipped to understand that information can be stored on a **'grain of sand'**, the smallest form of a crystal. We are now beginning to realise that almost nothing seems impossible. Like in space travel, 30 years ago we could only visit the moon. Yet within one generation we are now planning on sending people to Mars, and in the future maybe further planets... Who knows where we can end up; after overcoming gravity and with new methods of propulsion maybe the old expression that 'the sky is the limit' should be replaced with 'there are no limits'! I am no rocket scientist, but I feel that the more we learn about space and its possibilities, the more we begin to understand the 'energy' that animates our body; the VITAL FORCE, in homœopathic language. This auric layer of the 'Soul' is like the second etheric template of the physical body, only on a higher plane and much bigger than the first one, which is right next to the body (discussed earlier in section 4.3). Like the 'Throat Chakra' it vibrates to the colour BLUE relating to a wavelength of 440–495 nm.

The more developed a person is on their spiritual path, the stronger this auric field will be. (I once read that Buddha's aura extended approximately 200 miles out from his body!) Since it is not going to dissolve into 'thin air', we have to naturally conclude that this 'Life Force', or 'Chi', might indeed be 'recycled' and born again – 'Reincarnation'. Nothing is ever wasted in the Universe; everything is there for a purpose and what is wrong with coming back to this school called EARTH to learn a little more each time? Some might feel that coming back to Earth is like returning to HELL! This could indeed be true for some people but 'life is what you make of it' is the saying and if you choose to make it 'hellish' then who do you think is to blame? In the Bible Jesus says that we see the 'splinter' in the eyes of others, but the 'beam' in our own we miss!

'Feeling misunderstood all the time' is associated with remedies like Carcinosin, Ignatia, Mercury and Sulphur, while for 'being critical of parents, teachers and friends' Ignatia, Mercury and Sepia are at hand to solve such a problem. With some of our Polychrests we can see how we can break these cycles of blaming others for our own misfortunes, making the 're-cycling' – this life a happy affair this time around! Next we will look at two more subtle bodies.

The BUDDHIC and CAUSAL BODY – Energy Bodies Nos. 6 & 7

After the **Etheric Body** we have two more subtle bodies; the **BUDDHIC BODY**, which we could call our 'Higher Self', and the **CAUSAL BODY, the God within 'from which all cometh'.**

The Causal Body is the 'I AM', the 'Alpha and Omega', the beginning and the end; we should honour and love. Here, we are 'attached' to the rest of the Universe by the **'Silver Cord'**. When this cord is cut PRANA, the universal energy/breath, is withdrawn from the physical body and the 'Spirit' will leave the body via the Crown Chakra.

At birth the silver cord enters through the Crown Chakra to go down the spine. On the physical level this stimulates the nervous system. The expecting mother is very much aware of this happening when for the first time the baby moves, called 'quickening'. Not that the foetus did not move before, but this time it is different, it 'moves' the mother too, bringing her great joy and excitement. The embryo is no longer something unknown within, it moves and this makes it a little person one can talk to silently or otherwise. Of course nowadays with ultrasound scanning the expecting mother has most likely a picture of her unborn long before this event, yet the delight of 'feeling' the baby for the first time is no less dramatic.

In the Lord's Prayer the first sentence 'Our Father, who art in Heaven, Hallowed be thy Name' addresses the level at the Causal body and strengthens it. It was given to us to show us how the seven human principles are fully met within this prayer. The rest of the Lord's Prayer will deal with the other layers of the aura and will be explained in the last chapter. All the same I will finish the whole prayer here: 'Thy kingdom come, Thy will be done, on earth as it is in heaven. Give us today our daily bread, and forgive us our trespasses, as we forgive those who trespass against us. And lead us not into temptation, but deliver us from evil, for thine is the kingdom, and the power and the glory for ever and ever. Amen. (Please refer to the full explanation in the final chapter.)

A little more information about the **Buddhic Body**, where we can find our 'NIRVANA', providing we believe in the sentence: 'Thy Kingdom come, thy will be done'. It was given to us to keep us in touch with our higher self: Not **my will**, which is the inflated **EGO** and belongs to the lower chakra, but the ego, that animates us. We need this ego in order to incarnate. It is part of the 'father' energy that motivates all our activities.

We have all come to Earth to help humanity to progress and by doing so support our own progress, increasing our knowledge of what it is like to be restricted in a body on a very low vibration in comparison to other realms. As a 'race' we can learn from other races, but most of all we must learn from our own mistakes and follies. This sixth layer of the celestial body is the 'second' emotional body on the spiritual plane. Only when we have overcome the 'lower' **desire body** are we able to reach this level of perfection. Highly evolved souls, like **Jesus, Buddha,** and **Krishna** to name just some, were not the only **Souls**; many others were also aware of their mission and were in touch with others on this level. What level? Can we 'measure' this level, one might ask?

Yes, we can and David R. Hawkins, M.D., Ph.D. has provided us with answers in his book: 'The Eye of the I from which nothing is hidden'. (I highly recommend this book to anyone interested in this subject). A table presented in this book demonstrates which numbers relate to certain emotions, as well as to **God-views, Life-views, Levels** attained and the **'Process'** or reaction we have in connection with these. Kinesiology, or muscle testing, was used as a tool to arrive at these figures. The numbering system is explained in the book is on a scale up to **1000**, with lower 'scores' relating to less desirable qualities. I will just pick a few to mention here:

At only **20** points your level is '**Shame**' and the emotions are humiliations, with the process to free yourself of these being 'elimination'. Who would not want to eliminate shame? Next, let us consider 'Grief'.

'Grief', which would give you **75** points; here you would suffer lots of 'anxiety' and you would subsequently most likely choose 'withdrawal' to avoid this. When thinking of grief and withdrawing from the world the remedy Natrum-Muriaticum immediately springs to mind, for anyone familiar with Homœopathy (when faced with patients that lock the door to be alone with their grief). Imagine being stuck on such a low vibration (only 75 out of 1000); taking a remedy will aid the person to elevate to the next level.

The next emotions of **'Anger', 'Hate'** and **'Aggression'**, however, only scores **150** and leave a lot to be desired, and **'Pride'** with **170** on a scale up to 1000 points is not much better either! Only when one can find **'Courage'**, which goes together with 'empowerment', will one get over the magic **200** mark! According to Hawkins **200** as a figure is very important as humanity as a whole needs to get over this mark in order to progress. Anything below repeats the same old pattern (maybe even lifetime after lifetime). The emotions belong to the desire body and keep us 'locked in' – remember that letting go of the emotions was the 'gateway to freedom'. With every 40 or 50 points that you can climb up this scale you improve/increase the vibration to a staggering 1000, which was the level of Jesus who came to tell us about 'love' and 'truth'.

The figure **500**, half way up the table, stands for **LOVE**, while **350** stands for **'Forgiveness'**, which is the first step to unconditional love. When having reached a level of **600** points there is 'completeness' and joy, serenity and transfiguration. This sounds very 'inviting' to be part of such a grand scheme.

Having read this book (and many others on this topic), I feel that we can all attain this level and that this is what we call the 'Golden Age', which was promised to us by Jesus. The energies of all of humanity have indeed moved up and up, especially since the Harmonic Convergence in 1989. This was a get together of 'like-minded-souls' who, through prayers and meditation, came together to help us raise our energies. Therefore there are no excuses for ourselves not to try harder to improve our intuition and to 'shift' ourselves onto the next level of awareness. If we carry on this path and do not mess things up again, we should all get there! Moving from a third dimensional being into fourth and fifth dimensions is possible and alternative therapies will help us to overcome negative emotions and 'life views', as well as the God-view, in which 'our' God punishes and condemns people for their misgivings.

Yet there is no such thing as a 'free lunch', so the saying goes. We all have to work on it and as a Homœopath I feel that we have remedies with the energy and even the potencies to match this level. A 50 M to a CM would meet this level to help humanity.

However, not just Homœopathy has been given to us as a tool to help, to encourage the higher self and to amalgamate with the lower ego and the lower realms. The tool kit is now full of other energy-work related therapies, including: Reiki, first practised by Dr Mikao Usui (1865-1926); Cranial Sacral, developed by Dr William Garner Sutherland in the 1930s; Reflexology, a foot massage relating to pressure points and organ zones of the body on the feet, also developed in the last Century; and 'Golden Grid', introduced as recently as 1986 – a non-touch therapy in which only the Auric Field with its different energy bodies is worked on. These are just a few 'alternative' therapies on offer and there are many others, truly too numerous to mention them all.

As long as they are each practised with LOVE and the desire to help your fellow human being, all of these therapies are valid and show that we really care. Just like we need to look after GAIA, mother Earth (if we do not take care of her, how can she 'nurture' us?), if we look at ourselves as children of God, coming from Spirit, we are also children of the mother 'Gaia' in the physical and all the levels need to be addressed 'as above so below', for total well-being.

These last two energy bodies vibrate to the colours of INDIGO and PURPLE of wavelengths of 410-440 and 380-410 nm, also associated with the 'Third Eye' and the 'Crown Chakra'.

Within these seven bodies are the seven chakras, the wheels to keep the nadis (energy channels) and meridian (rivers of bioelectric currents – also known as chi) energy flowing. The nadis (there are 144,000 of them) are channels of prana (energy/life force) that run through our body, which are similar to the meridians used in Chinese medicine. Such meridians are, for example, used in Acupuncture (the pressure points), and are another way to free 'blocked energy', helping people to move on. Any blockage here is a hindrance as it becomes a focal point to the person, rather than seeing the bigger picture; and the 'picture', like our aura, is a very big one. With everything mentioned so far we have still only touched on it in a minute way. Just like in Homœopathy, the learning seems to be endless when you think of how many plants and animals there are in the world that have not yet had a 'proving' as a remedy. Considering the 3,000 or so remedies we have at present, this is only just the 'beginning'. Maybe in the future we will not need to 'prove' anything at all, as meditational provings will give us all the answers we need. Plus by 'tuning into the aura' of a patient we should be able to pick up in which layer the energy is stuck and thus provide the clues to the remedies and potency needed. There are exciting times ahead.

Chapter FIVE

Introducing the CHAKRAS

CHAKRAS, the Sanskrit word for 'wheels', are force centres; vortices like miniature Suns emanating energy from the body, functioning like valves or pumps. Each chakra has a profound influence and effect on the mind and body of a person, as is recognised by Eastern Philosophies such as Hinduism, Tibetan Buddhism, and in Ayurveda or Yoga.

Chakras are generally not visible except to visionaries such as Leadbeater (1854-1934), for example, who was a great psychic, and supporter of the Theosophical Society in England, and who drew pictures of these seven major energy centres. As far as I am aware, Leadbeater was one of the first to describe them to modern Western Society, which he did in his book 'The Chakras': **"Though the mouth of the flower-like bell of the chakra is on the surface of the etheric body, the stem of the trumpet-like blossom always springs from a centre in the spinal chord".**

From a medical point of view chakras do not exist, yet in the body we find bundles of nerve cells known as the ganglions that are located where we find the chakras. These ganglions are partly fibrous and partly nerve cells and on an energetic level they are attached to each other. The chains of ganglia connected to the sympathetic nervous systems are:

4 sacral ganglia activate the 'Hypogastric plexus'.
These are linked to the rectum, genital organ and the bladder.
The Base Chakra
The virtue here is PURITY while the passion is PRIDE.

4 lumbar ganglia activate the 'Mesenteric plexus'.
These are linked with the solar plexus,
Through the solar plexus they are linked to the stomach, the small intestine,
the liver, pancreas and kidneys.
The Sacral Chakra
The virtue here is JUSTICE while the passion is GREED.

12 dorsal ganglia activate the 'Solar plexus'.
Through the solar plexus they are linked to the lungs.
The Solar Plexus
The virtue here is LOVE while the passion is ANGER.

3 cervical ganglia, also called the 'Cardiac plexus'.
These are linked to the heart.
The Heart Chakra
The virtue here is WISDOM while the passion is LUST.

3 intra-cranial ganglia, called the 'Cervical plexus'.
These are located on the path of the trigeminal nerve.
The Throat Chakra
The virtue here is TRUTH while the passion is ATTACHMENT.

The upper two Chakras are the Third Eye and the Crown Chakra.
Altogether there are 26 ganglia, divided into five groups. These five groups in turn are linked to 'five' virtues, as noted above. The five are also linked to the elements of **Earth, Water, Fire, Air** and **Ether**, while the last two chakras, the **Third Eye** and the **Crown Chakra**, are supplied with nerves from the **'Carotid plexus'**. Its main function is

to control the breathing so that an adequate supply of oxygen is maintained to the tissues of the body.

However, having mentioned only five pairs of ganglia as they branch out from the spine and energise the chakras, when considering the Bowel Nosodes we of course include the upper two as well. Even though there are more than the seven major chakras (additional chakras to these, for example, are found in the hands, under the feet and behind the knees), for the exercise of this book we will restrict the knowledge to the seven well-known ones.

Energy flows from the chakras in and out of the body and could be called, as Hahnemann did, the **'Vital force'**. Other authors give these energies different names, but in Homœopathy we are very familiar with this terminology and understand that the remedies work on this level. These **Energy Bodies** or **Auras** could also be called our 'spiritual skin'.

Long before Leadbeater re-introduced the chakras and the 'outer' energy of the body to 'modern' society the Greek philosopher Plato tried to relate stories with the 'unseen' world in mind. In his parable of the 'cave people' Plato talks about people living in a cave who have been fettered by the ankles and the neck since early childhood. With their backs to the cave entrance and facing the cave wall they have no idea of the world 'outside'. All they ever see are 'shadows'! The shadows on the wall of the cave are produced by the flickering of a fire in the centre of the cave, yet behind their backs figures move past the cave entrance or near the fire. These 'shadows' have become reality to those poor prisoners: If they were to be taken by the hand and shown the real world outside their little niche in the cave they would be blinded. Firstly, they would not be used to such dazzling light and would be blinded by the brightness outside. Secondly, the splendour would be too much to take in. They might turn away and run back to the darkness and 'comfort' zone of the cave: It would all be very confusing to see the magnificence of nature and they might think they have 'gone crazy'.

Imagine, however, that one member of the group freed himself, curious of what else there might be beyond the cave. Having made his way past the fire (the sacred fire – connecting us to spirit) he gradually was able to 'see'. (I write gradually, as enlightenment usually takes place by assimilation of spiritual knowledge, rather than coming as an overnight success.) He absorbs his new unknown territory little by little, realising that there is more to his (or this) world than his narrow cave, or rather 'narrow mindedness' (our comfort zone).

I like to use this parable as a guide to compare it with the chakras: The first two (base and sacral chakras) represent the **'cave'** with its shadow world and the world of illusions. The base chakra is certainly needed to 'anchor' us in the world of matter; into the physical body. The sacral chakra is for our 'expansion', to move on, or rather to propel us forward. Unfortunately we misuse it too often by tying ourselves to earthly possessions, sex and addictions, all of which take our attention away from the real goals. Like the cave people we watch the shadows, almost predicting which of the usual shapes might appear next, yet with no interest to go past the fire to discover the world behind our backs. We, the cave dwellers, are full of fears and anticipation (base chakra issues) and prefer the comfort zone we know so well.

However, great rewards are in store for the loner who breaks free and overcomes the **fire** of the solar plexus, since the solar plexus is the chakra which motivates the heart by its virtue of LOVE. By moving into and opening the heart chakra the next step to the throat is not too difficult; like arriving at the opening of the cave, we are full of awe. Seeing the beauty outside the cave with the heart chakra open, unconditional love for others and

54

for the self will follow suit. Having experienced this we would want to return and tell the rest of the people of the 'Garden of Eden' on our doorstep. The feeling is like 'compassion for all' and one would want to share it. As Plato points out the one **outside** would rather do the meanest job possible than to be tied up back in the cave. Yet in order to tell the others what he had seen the loner would have to return; you can have three guesses of what their reaction might be upon hearing what the he had seen!

Few might listen and some might even take it on board, eager to make changes. Some would laugh, calling him 'crazy', while others might say he was blinded by the light and that his eyes had played tricks on him. Fanatical others might even beat or kill him (out of the fear of having to face new situations and having to adapt). As history has shown so often, the messenger reporting new information was killed, and not just in the 'Dark Ages'; it still goes on by fanatics.

If we could truly see the spirit world represented as the outside of the cave from which all stems, we would see that the shadows are just a dim picture of the original before it was manifested in matter and we would understand that we live in this 'shadow world' most of the time (at least when we are awake; in sleep we do visit the 'other world').

By repeatedly clearing blockages of traumas, toxins, metabolic disorders etc. from the chakras with the help of the Bowel Nosodes, as well as the related remedies (even if I have to admit that miracles sometimes have taken place without the aid of homœopathic remedies and numerous books have been written about these, however in most cases progress takes time), little by little we can overcome our **'delusions'**, fears and negative emotions, and leave the cave and be **'free'**.

Freedom includes freedom of choice, which is the very essence that we have when we are in the physical body on this planet. Let us use it wisely and truthfully! The virtues of the heart and throat chakras are **Wisdom and Truth**; these are the qualities that we should aim to achieve when opening the third eye in order to become a visionary and, when the crown chakra is fully open, a saintly person.

The BASE CHAKRA – No. 1

The Physical body = the most dense

Planet: SATURN   Element: EARTH   Metal: LEAD   Sense: SMELL

The Colour is RED with a wavelength of 625-700 nm.

Zodiac: Aquarius and Capricorn are the Saturn months
(this is important to know when it comes to the tissue salts as support remedies)

The Musical note is: C = 4 beats/vibration

Petals 4 (petals refer to the spokes of the chakra, the energy wheel, where the number of petals in Eastern Philosophy represents the level of spiritual development; notice that we start off here with only **four** petals, while the crown chakra has 972 petals).

The **BASE CHAKRA or GROUND chakra is <u>situated at the base of the spine</u>** and is **connected to the Adrenal Glands** producing the hormone known as **adrenalin**, ready for 'fight or flight' at times of stress. **Adrenal Energy:** when we live too much on adrenal energy we not only deplete this chakra of energy, but we can 'knock-out' the crown chakra – 'as above so below'.

The BASE is the Foundation – 'the launch pad'
Primary function: to ground the spirit in the material world,
to be well-rooted in this incarnation.

We need the physical body in order to function/exist on Earth – it is the point of power for the 'animal man'. The minerals and trace elements provide the structure to the body and these we share with the animal and plant kingdoms, thus the skeletal system is of major importance when supporting this chakra with remedies. **Coccyx injury** can cause a blockage in this **chakra.**

In our evolution, the long process through the various kingdoms, we have 'moved' from the 'group soul' of the animal to a more feeling and rational being. However, at the level of the Base Chakra some people still behave like animals and listening to the news nowadays, which are more often negative than positive, one sometimes wonders 'is it not like a jungle out there?'(Is this the urban jungle of the modern city?)

The Base Chakra is fed by the hypo-gastric plexus, also called the 'lumbar' or 'sacral ganglia', as mentioned before, and links us to the physical world. It controls the **legs**, sending the energy down the legs into the earth to root it below and between our **feet**. Like a ship in a harbour casting the anchor it helps to connect us to the **magnetism of the earth**.

This energy flow needs to match the alchemy of the body to increase its vibration. The word alchemy means 'casting of metals' and it is well known that the medieval alchemists were searching for the 'elixir of life' by <u>turning 'base' metals into **Gold**</u>. I would like to think that one way of turning **this base metal** into gold could be found in remedies, since the metal for this chakra is **LEAD**. Being the heaviest metal it can cause real problems not just with the <u>skeletal system</u> but in the <u>mental sphere</u> too if there is an accumulation of lead in the body.

The Planet SATURN

Saturn is symbolised by the skeleton with the scythe in his hand, who embodies 'Father Time' and is attributed to death; the sickle cuts off the strands of life. Old pictures often portray Saturn as the 'grim reaper' who calls for us all at the end of our days here on earth and who is the very thing most people have the greatest fear of. Too much **LEAD** in the system will increase the 'fear of death', as we know from our proving picture of the remedy called Plumbum, which is not surprising since it is one of the most poisonous toxins known to man. It accumulates in the body tissues, primarily in the bones causing them to thicken.

In the brain it leads to a reduced intelligent quotient (IQ) and in severe cases to convulsions and coma, resulting in death. Thus the reason to leave the 'heaviness' of lead behind us and move up to the higher chakras makes sense, which is the 'transmutation' of the old alchemists. To do 'alchemy' in this way seems almost too easy, would you not agree? It takes the fun out of the searching for the 'elixir of life'. However, I feel that this is only one way to do it and there are others, I am sure. It is like 'slaying the dragon'; you will need more than just good will and a sword. You become a <u>creator of ideas</u> of how to go about it, and our homœopathic toolkit is full of remedies, old and new, with hundreds of books available from which information and facts can be drawn from, with the 'proving pictures' and clinical feed-back necessary to help humanity.

Saturn <u>is also the organiser, the builder</u>, indeed <u>the architect of things to come</u>. Saturn takes 28 years to move through our birth sign, or rather Sun sign, and with this arrives for the first time when we have grown into adulthood. At this time Saturn will 'question' us 'if we have learnt our lesson well' (so far)? The second time Saturn comes around will be at age 56, often a time when we start planning 'as and when' to retire. If we are fortunate enough to live so long, the third time Saturn returns will be at age 84. At this ripe age, however, we might not want to make life-changing decisions, yet we should be wise enough to get 'the house into order' and prepare to leave the earth plane as and when appropriate. In some cases this departure can be very sudden, while in other cases people linger and yet others still enjoy what are now called the 'golden years', all depending upon how active they are in mind and body. Usually, the more able the skeletal system, the more active the mind will be. Actively moving the muscle tissues and keeping in good shape will prevent stagnation in the lymphatic system and will automatically lessen the toxins that would otherwise accumulate and slowly poison the body.

For your own curiosity be aware of changes taking place in your lifetime at or around those birthdays, give or take a year or two.

The Element EARTH

Earth the 'material' is the densest of the five elements and provides the body with structure by supplying it with the minerals and plants necessary for it to sustain life. The gravity field surrounding the Earth is sometimes called 'Earth's prana', connecting Earth to Heaven. Mother Earth symbolises the female principle of Yin and represents fertility and nurturing. The glyph of the earth is the square ■ (the perfect launch-pad).

Our Earth as a planet represents the 'third dimension', which is the 'testing laboratory' for the rest of our Solar System (according to D. Cannon's book 'The Convoluted Universe'). Earth is matter, but all matter contains spirit and is electrical in function, manifesting in different forms because of varying rates of vibration or speed. This very condition that exists in the material plane has its counterpart and pattern in the cosmic or spiritual plane: **matter, force** and **mind**, or 'creative consciousness'. God moved and said 'let there be light', and there was light; this is the light or force within the body; the **matter that animates**. When light leaves the body rigor mortis ensues and the matter of the body can be returned to 'Mother Earth'.

Matter comprises atoms, atoms are energy, energy is spirit, and spirit is God. Atoms, molecules, cells, and matter change but the essence, the spirit, does not. The movement (the vibration) of this atomic structure is the manifestation of the creator: 'Know ye not that ye are the temple of God and that the spirit of God dwells in you?'

Earth in Chinese medicine is one of the five elements making up the building blocks of the universe. Earth is involved in personal transformation; it represents a phase of learning in our personal evolution, as it is the 'free will' which was bestowed to foster 'creativity'. It is up to us to establish stability here or create chaos. **Positive Qualities are: Stamina and physical drive – all is well.** Its action is to establish order, to preserve, test, to discipline and to solidify. Responsible, idealistic, moral, orderly, integrity, endurance and fortitude are words which spring to mind. **Earth** controls water, which is the element of the next chakra.

Tension here has to do with issues of: Security/Survival/Trust/Money/Home/Family/Job.

However, not just the family will give us the security we need to feel happy in this world; the nation we are born into also will 'shape' us. Blockages here can be caused by vaccination and drugs of any kind, including the so called 'pleasure drugs', which space us out and may make us lose our way.

Of course any **trauma**, emotional or physical – abuse of any sort, which makes us feel insecure – can have a huge impact on this centre and can turn us into a VICTIM 'state' for the rest of our life. Just because of the insecurity we had to face in childhood we might for the rest of our life blame others for our misfortunes if we do not get help here. Abuse always creates FEAR, and this chakra is 'driven' by the adrenal glands into HYPERACTIVITY, or the opposite inertia. To shut away the fear the mind goes 'blank', which might be the only way of coping with it. Words like sorrowful, gloomy, pessimistic, and opinionated with fixed ideas, as well as insecurity would show how much the mind suffers. **For those who FEAR, the Bach Flower Essences: Aspen, Cherry Plum, Mimulus, Red Chestnut** and **Rock Rose** can help (for those who like to add flower essences as an extra).

There are many different **Flower Essences** available from different parts of the World, too numerous to mention. Due to the vibration within these essences they are here to help us to progress, to overcome 'grief' from the past and to move away from the negative 'Victim state'.

If we were nurtured in the first seven years of our lives, feeling secure in a home with a loving family around us, later in life we should make good mothers and fathers for the next generation and pass on this sense of security. Why did I mention the first seven years? It is the time that the first energy body, which is part of our subtle bodies, will manifest itself. Consequently the fewer traumas we have during our early childhood, which can cause this energy body to tear, the stronger will be the 'shield' that we will carry with us for the rest of our life.

As this chakra has to do with our 'skeletal system' we have to consider the bones, including the spinal column, the neck, shoulders, and joints, both large and small. Also included is the skin and teeth. To have healthy teeth children need vital minerals and therefore we can consider the Sarcode 'Parathyroid' if a child's teeth decay early and if they complain about 'growing pains'. This Sarcode will help them to assimilate the required minerals better and provide a strong foothold for a long life.

Other physical problems, apart from lead and radiation poisoning, are mineral deposits in the form of kidney stones, gout, arthritis and rheumatism with stiffness and deformed joints. Liver congestion starts here with gall-stones, which begins with tiny crystals produced in the liver before they are deposited in the gall-bladder.

Weight loss, weakness and emaciation leading to degeneration and chronic diseases for lack of minerals and trace elements can certainly have their origin in this chakra. Blockages can also lead to high blood pressure and hot flushes, not just in this chakra but also in the opposite one, the crown chakra; this is one reason why the new flower remedy LOTUS works so extremely well for acute menopausal heat rushes to the head. This flower grows in the 'earth element' and reaches through the element 'water' to the 'air' above, where the flower opens with its petals like a 'fire' resting on water. In the remedy picture of Lotus this can help to 'release the heat within'.

The Colour RED – wavelength 625-700 nm

The colour RED warms and stimulates the blood, which *carries* the life-force; it purifies the blood in a very profound way – like **Thuja** – but **Red** works on a different wavelength from Thuja, which is called the 'tree of life'. As mentioned earlier the **Ego** resides in the blood.

Haemorrhages and inflammation in the blood, all redness/heat/swelling will respond to this remedy. Good for burns and sunburns! This remedy also works well with leukaemia and anaemia, relating to circulation/blood vessels/heart.

Red is a grounding colour, especially after a trauma or for people feeling 'spacey' and disconnected. It has the slowest vibration (longest wavelength) and the most dense energy field. It raises a person's energy out of its inertia back into action and addresses their fears, bringing back courage. For an overactive person who sees 'red' all the time it might be better to choose a cooler colour to calm them.

Physical problem: rectal (constipation and piles) and urinary problems; varicose veins. General: depression and debility.

The Metal LEAD

The Latin name of this soft malleable metallic element is **Plumbum**, which gives us its elemental symbol **Pb**. This is also the name of the remedy made from **Lead**, which is not only very heavy but very toxic, too. The description of the remedy picture is in fact not a 'pretty' one and in the 'mind' rubric we have statements such as: 'Mental depression'; 'Fear of being assassinated' or 'of being poisoned'; 'dementia and loss of memory'; as well as 'hysterics, only while being watched and screams from time to time'; plus 'physical labour exhausts the mind'!

Physical problems can start in infancy with 'marasmus in infants', or a 'hernia of the navel' when the navel feels retracted and the 'abdomen is tense or retracted'. The face of the infant looks pale and emaciated. Both young and old can suffer from 'constipation with hard stool', which is 'black with urging and spasms of anus', and 'stubborn constipation of infant with colic' is also listed.

In the mouth a distinct blue line can be seen along the margin of the gums, which is the typical sign of lead poisoning. As so many old houses (at least in England) used to have lead piping for their water supply this is often observed in England, especially in the elderly.

In the limbs we have paralysis, atrophied single muscles or limbs, like 'wrist drop'. Cramping of the muscles and/or ice-cold hands and feet are all indications that there is no flow of energy anywhere. To give an example here, I will relay the case of a relative of mine in Germany who complained about 'Intermittent Claudification' where her legs at times just did not want to move. I searched for a reason as well as for a remedy. During our discussion it turned out that she had worked as a cashier at a petrol station for over ten years, of course breathing in fumes that were heavily laced with lead at the time. We were able to clear the blockage caused by this metal by giving her Plumbum 30c, as well as Morgan Pure 200c for the congestion in this chakra.

By giving Plumbum in potency to detoxify from lead we can start the energy to flow again, from the base chakra upwards. This will lighten the load, moving up one chakra after the other until it reaches the heart chakra, where the GOLD is found: The gold is the goal, where we 'shine' and have compassion for all and everything. Selfishness is left behind, as is the 'fear of death' state as mentioned at the beginning of this chapter, which finds its expression in the remedy **LEAD** and in this chakra with the planet **SATURN**.

Bowel Nosodes – Morgan Pure and Morgan Bach

Keynote: Congestion in skin and circulation, and the emotion is **FEAR.**

Congestion in the chakra can be caused by FEAR, arising from a very frightful event or a situation we experienced in early life that put us into this 'fearful state'. One such incident, for example, could be 'getting stuck in the birth canal' and having to be physically helped into this world. In this case, in order to loosen this congestion caused due to the pressure and anxiety experienced (and anxiety it caused to all present), apart from using Homœopathy to 'get over it' Cranial Sacral therapy would also be very conducive, to be saved from a lifelong 'lack of flow down the spine'. Both mother and child would benefit from the remedies, as well as from a 'hands on' session with a Cranial Sacral therapist. Otherwise, if not addressed at the time, a physical as well as a mental/emotional blockage could result right from the start of life.

FEAR often comes from 'insecurity', either in early life or later. Any incident can contribute to the many fears that people may have, be it a fear of diseases, an anxiety of 'facing the world' by 'speaking up for oneself', or for children the dread of 'being bullied' at school. For the latter, without the support of adults to sort out the problem depression in the child may arise, which in the worst cases may even lead to thoughts of suicide. The child no longer feels 'safe' in a place of learning and this can have a lasting effect, with this burden being carried around like a heavy rucksack until it is addressed with remedies or other therapies, helping to lessen the load.

CONGESTION can be in many parts of the body, for example manifesting in the head with headaches, in the bones with stiffness of joints (rheumatism), or in the liver and gallbladder giving problems of gallstones. Liver congestion can also lead to the development of varicose veins, as well as haemorrhoids. Women after the menopause may experience high blood pressure and **hot flushes**, and vertigo is often a problem, too. In the **Uterus** congestion can take place in the form of fibroids or polyps. The **congestion** can of course also be created by 'medication' that blocks the system. An example of this would be constipation as a side-effect of taking antibiotics, or a vaccination causing a disconnection to the 'root' – our home-base. This is like a tree without a strong root that will suffer more easily when adverse weather conditions sweep the land.

Congestion shows itself in skin problems at a very young age. Eczema in a baby is a very common symptom these days and knowing that Graphites belongs to this chakra, we can see how this bowel flora in potency could help in cases where Graphites is the indicated remedy. Later these children might complain of growing pains (as mentioned above), especially in the long bones of the legs. This too points to the base chakra, remembering that the skeletal system, the legs and the feet are the appendages here. Once we realise that congestion, the 'key-note' for these Bowel Nosodes, has taken place here other metals like Aluminium, Cadmium and Strontium are also remedies to consider. More indications are provided in the table.

Remedies related to the Base Chakra

Remedies from the Vegetable Kingdom:	**Cean., Con., Symph., Thios.**
Remedies from the Mineral Kingdom:	**Cadm-s., Calc-c., Calc-f., Calc-p., Hecla., Graph., Petr., Sil., Stront-c.**
Remedies from the Metal Kingdom:	**Alum., Ars., Plb.**

The Nosodes:	**Carc.,** *Morgan Bach & Pure,* **Lepro., Ring-w., Psor.,** and **Tub-b.**
The Sarcodes:	**Adrenal Gland & Kidney.**
New Remedies:	**Ayahuasca, Chalcancite, Clay, Copper Beach, Holly, Lotus, Lumbricus, Jet, Moonstone, Oak, Obsidian, Rose Quartz, Sea Holly, Sequoia and Silverfish.**
Other Remedies:	**Sarsaparilla** and **Berberis** as support for the adrenal glands. **Manganum** to strengthen the nerves. **Digitalis** to be considered if there is high blood pressure. **Mag-Carb.** and **Nat-Carb,** as they both have the carbon element (part of our basic structure); as well as **Carbo-veg, Carbo-an.,** and **Carbo Sulph.**

4

The SACRAL CHAKRA – No. 2

The SACRAL CHAKRA belonging to the Emotional Body

Element: WATER   Planet: JUPITER   Metal: TIN   Sense: TASTE

The Colour is ORANGE with a wavelength of 595-635 nm

Zodiac: Sagittarius and Pisces are the Jupiter months.

The Musical note is: D = 3 beats/vibrations
Petals 6

The Sacral Chakra is situated below the navel in the region of the lumbar spine:
The Glands are the Gonads governing the reproductive system.
In women, the ovaries and uterus; in men, the testicles and prostate.

Primary function: Pleasure, well being, sexuality and abundance!
Relationships from intimate to superficial all need to be learned from.

The **Sacral Chakra** is also known as the **'Polarity Chakra'**. The power of **'illusion'** on this chakra is second to none and is analogous to Hollywood and the film industry, which is a world full of illusions! (Some would say that our whole life is just an 'illusion' as our home is not here on Earth at all; it is like writing another story in a book called 'Life'. However, this is open to discussion.)

Hollywood creates great escapism from the real world, with a make-believe replacement world where almost every story has (or at least used to have) a 'happy ending', like in fairy tales. I say in 'almost' every film, as this has changed over the years, maybe due to our greater 'spiritual' understanding and opening up those extra 'channels' now available to us.

Increasingly we realise and know better that a challenge leads to a course that we need to follow and is not necessarily attached to a positive outcome. Sometimes we only learn the hard way, with more obstacles in the way than we bargained for. Yet, it is only by facing up to and overcoming these difficulties by being brave and acknowledging that it is for the benefit of learning, that we will grow in our understanding of the purpose of life. It is like at school where the tasks becomes more difficult with every year you attend and indeed it would be very boring if this would not be so, would you not agree? If you repeated the first grade year after year you would become the disruptive child due to boredom. No doubt in this situation you would want to be 'stretched' and learn something new, rather than the same old lesson again! If we translate this into reincarnation the same applies; we need something to motivate us to progress to the next grade.

Having a break now and again by taking a 'holiday' from the hard journey can be the right action to take, before becoming totally exhausted from the daily chores and trials. These days, with easy access to the rest of the world, we can learn from the rest of the population and enhance our own understanding off different religions and customs. This in turn helps us to create a vast 'global village', where we care for what happens to fellow human beings and where we can send help when disasters occur. The process of being responsible for others is to be a true human and not to get 'lost' in a world of 'make-believe', which we can also create for ourselves when we pretend that all is well when this is truly not the case.

Getting 'lost' in a 'false world' of our own delusions is like playing games on a computer that are so realistic that we become a 'creator of a world of illusions second to none'. Yet to become addicted to these and not get on with the real 'job at hand' often causes a great deal of conflict; for instance, a teenager choosing this route of 'relaxation' and escapism (as has been well documented on television) will bring despair to the parents. They seem disinterested and 'unbothered' about the real life issues. In teenagers this is often a short phase of growing up and as parents we might have to tolerate this 'trial period', especially since teenagers will confront and test us to see how far they are allowed to 'go down that road'. As long as we can show them that our love for them is still strong despite these temporary differences and conflicts. We can help them to focus on the greater picture. If we can allow them to discover how to master their own life and become 'co-creators' in this, rather than a 'game', we can consider ourselves to have done a 'good job' as parents. We must not forget that not so long ago we adults were teenagers too, and that the time of adolescent is just another phase of growing up.

In terms of remedies we can think about Berlin Wall, which can help to improve this kind of 'addictive behaviour'. With this remedy we can overcome the 'wall' that has developed between parents and children due to lack of communication, when the **games** become the greater focus rather than the guidance of the parents and what they are trying to teach.

Coming back to the world of 'glitz and glamour' Las Vegas and other gambling cities alike may also be seen as worlds of 'make-believe': Used by holidaymakers to 'get away from it all', i.e. away from reality. With no clocks anywhere to be seen in the Casinos it is easy to move from day to night to day again without any sense of time. This of course is the idea behind 'getting lost' in this world, where everyone is supposed to be a 'winner'! The question that needs to be asked is who is the real winner here? Yet, we have to agree there are always two sides to every coin, which brings me to polarity.

Polarity is expressed through **Motions** and **Movement** and not by **e-Motions,** which are a waste of energy! Yet, by motions we move forward and 'create' our life as this is the Chakra of CREATION. In this sense Hollywood is part of this 'creativity' and there is no need to condemn it in any way; it is an industry providing jobs and allows artists to produce films that make 'their dreams come true'. As consumers we can go and watch their creation or not, as it may be. We can give them 'awards' for their achievements or ignore or even condemn what was presented, depending on our viewpoint. Mentioning these two places above, Hollywood and Las Vegas, is not to 'pick on them' but is merely to demonstrate the power of this chakra, where pleasure and abundance are the primary function. There is a place of everything on this magnificent planet. Choices must be made on a daily basis of how to conduct one's own life, but also to consider what effect decisions might have on others. A positive conduct helps the flow of energy and can be inspiring to others.

The sacral chakra is of course also the **centre of procreation** and this creative centre should not be blocked by medication such as the 'anti-baby' pill or hormone replacement therapy (**HRT**) in later years. The menopause is another passage to maturity and by delaying the process through HRT we delay this natural flow. Is it really necessary to delay the menopause? And when would one like to have the menopause, at age 80? I am sure in most cases the answer would be 'no', especially when having to face possible side-effects, amongst which is a higher risk of thrombosis, possible liver damage and gallbladder problems, to name just a few. An insightful German book called 'Bittere Pillen' (harmful pills) gives information to over 3000 medicines and lists their possible therapeutic benefits, as well as their <u>known undesirable</u> effects on the human body, which could be the very reason why more and more people are searching for 'alternatives'.

In my mind Homœopathy provides a truly holistic approach, taking into consideration the physical symptoms, as well as the emotions from which they may have arisen and the 'delusion' the person is then stuck in. To demonstrate this I will use a fictitious case (that sadly happens far too often in real life), where a little girl was sexually abused by a family member, which still 'haunts her' 30 years later. First came the physical pain as a child, with emotions of hate, grief and anger, yet wondering what she had done wrong to 'deserve this'. Then later, still trying to understand and even trying to love the abuser, she either denies that it ever happened or seeks help. (This often only happens years later when sexual relationships become a problem.) However, the delusion that 'I am worthless', 'despised by others', or 'not even belonging to her own family' could be one result of what took place, with Platina being one of the remedies to 'redeem' her.

Tension here has to do with food and sex. (Too much of it – I want, I want, I want....... and I want it all the time!)

As this chakra is associated with the gonads, for obvious reasons we can expect fertility problems, uterine disorders and bladder problems. No expansion will take place if the reproductive organs are blocked. For most people extending the family is a natural progression in life that brings joy as well as responsibilities, which are part of our own growth. There is no recipe of how to be a good parent, yet by trying hard the rewards are to be had by living in harmony with all of those around us.

In terms of lack of development of this chakra ill effects may be seen after vaccinations, which also can affect the opposite chakra; the 'Third Eye'. This occurs when the pituitary gland becomes blocked as a result of damage from a vaccine, which may lead to eating disorders such as obesity or anorexia. Kidney and liver damage/cirrhosis, jaundice and hepatitis from too much alcohol also originate here. Additionally, gluttony leads to indigestion and gas in the intestine with 'bloating', which causes the classical Lycopodium symptom of feeling 'tightness in the waistline after a meal'. Gallstones arising from mal-assimilation of food, and low blood-sugar, which leads to diabetes, both commence in this chakra.

The 'Emotional body' is the second of our subtle bodies and is linked to the sacral chakra, which is associated with the gonads. It manifests itself from the age of seven to fourteen with the beginning of puberty. Although this can be a difficult time for both parents and teenagers alike, the primary function of the emotional body is to **feel good about oneself** and thus with the right kind of parental guidance these troublesome times can be taken as another step toward independence.

During this stage in our development we learn how to form relationships; with our parents, simple friendships, and later sexual partnerships, as well as business related associations. We should become skilled at controlling our emotions, yet we often see people getting carried away by their emotions and we describe them as carrying 'their heart on their sleeve'. Please consider here that these emotions do not relate to the heart chakra, but are the second chakra in 'motion', since the element is **Water**! Water needs to flow and so does this chakra. If it does not flow and becomes blocked we do not expand in the way that we are supposed to by stretching our abilities in every way, creating new 'ideas' and following them through.

Instead we might expand in the waistline through 'over-eating' and we may become 'over-emotional', creating a drama each time things do not go the way we desire. Too much sex, or acts of rape or incest as mentioned earlier, is of course abuse to this chakra and can have lifelong effects (with a person never having been well since). Greed for money and playing the 'power game' is also detrimental and a misuse of this chakra.

Learning to control our emotions can make us as regal as a 'King' or the 'Queen' and in 'control of life' and be able to guide others. Being in charge of our personal life also creates the wish to go out into the world, to change it, and to make it a better place for all to live in; this yearning comes from this chakra. Honour, trustworthiness, and true understanding of the world's religions take place in the Sacral Chakra when it is working well.

For those who feel **'loneliness'**, which comes from this chakra, the **Bach Flower Essences Inpatients, Heather** or **Water Violet** can help a person to progress and leave their sense of feeling sorry for themselves behind.

The Planet JUPITER

Jupiter is the largest planet in the solar system. It is 11 times the diameter of the earth, the fifth farthest from the Sun and is the second brightest planet in the night sky, plus it has 15 moons; no wonder Jupiter is associated with expansion, growth, and opportunity. Jupiter represents the higher mind, wisdom, enthusiasm, optimism, benevolence and generosity, and its action is to expand, persevere and increase on all levels. In mythology Jupiter is also known as 'Jove', which leads to the modern word of 'jovial'. This relates well to persons who are born under the sign of Jupiter, which according to astrologists is the happiest of the natal stars. To the ancient Greeks Jupiter was known as Zeus, who was the greatest of the gods.

With so many positive attributes mentioned above, when this chakra works well a person should be: Full **of vitality, lively, good tempered, witty, generous** and **humane** and **above all loyal!** However, when things go wrong they may be: Insecure, over-indulgent, and have a strong appetite, with greed and worry being very much felt here.

The Element WATER

Water is the simplest molecule of two hydrogen atoms and one oxygen atom = H_2O. It may be formed when an electrical spark passes through a mixture of these two gasses. Water gives birth to form and can be found in three states; solid as ice, liquid water, and gaseous as steam. Without water our planet would not be called the 'blue planet' and the diversity of life on Earth would not exist. Indeed civilisation is a 'by-product' of water, with towns and cities typically being built next to rivers, lakes, and oceans.

In Genesis it is written that 'the spirit of God hovered over the waters', which can be interpreted that God is part of every water molecule; every drop of water. As the human body is principally composed of water ($\approx 60 \%$ of our body is water) we can in turn relate that God is part of us, and we of Him.

The human life-cycle can be compared to that of the hydrological (water) cycle on Earth: Water vapour in the atmosphere forms clouds and the water droplets are eventually released to fall to the Earth's surface. Depending on where it falls this can be as snow on a mountainside or as rain on a meadow, cleansing and nurturing the earth as it joins a stream. This stream flows into a river, which ends up in a sea where it may evaporate back into the atmosphere and start again to form a cloud. In the human life-cycle we call this process reincarnation where we begin our journey in the stream, each time entering at a different place and therefore we experience different energies around us. Depending on where it meets the 'creative' element we have varieties in our appearances, such as our skin colour that can change from one lifetime to another, helping to give us a greater insight of our 'slight differences'; deep down we all stem from the same source and our DNA is that of a human and not of an animal nature. Even if we share some of the DNA with the animal kingdom no animal has yet been found to have exactly the same.

The glyph of water is a downward pointing triangle ▼.

From the research into water by the Japanese scientist Dr Masaru Emoto we can understand the subtle form of the energy he calls 'hado'. In his book 'The Hidden Messages of Water' Emoto shows stunning photographs of water crystals after they have been exposed to different words or music. When kind words or peaceful music are presented to the water beautiful crystals form, whereas water that has experienced unmelodic music (in this case 'heavy rock' music) or swearing, for example, it develops distorted crystals. This has given those who are interest in his finding a much greater insight and understanding of what happens to the fluids of our body and how we can influence them in either a constructive, positive way or in a destructive, negative manner. Therefore we are back to 'free choices' of how we treat or mistreat our body and these choices must be made on a daily basis.

In the human body the water element is represented by the kidneys and bladder, which maintain adequate moisture throughout. Internal moisture ensures the blood, salvia, sexual glands and hormones to be in balance. Water represents the deep, hidden depths of a person and in Chinese medicine it controls the fire, which is the element of the next chakra.

The Colour ORANGE – wavelength 595-635 nm

ORANGE, the mixture between red and yellow, is said to be a good colour remedy for the kidneys and the spleen. It is a colour that can increase the appetite for food for those having an eating disorder, but also increased the hunger for life and can help with problems of infertility, for example. This of course relates well to its associated chakra the sacral chakra, since the key word here is 'expansion'. The opposite of an eating disorder is of course eating too much food, being greedy and overindulging. This colour remedy can help to bring back the discipline and control, as well as better judgment for the right food.

The remedy should not to be given at night or bedtime due to its stimulating effect.

The Metal TIN

The white metal **TIN** is the alchemist of this chakra and as a remedy it is known by its Latin name **Stannum Metallicum.** On the periodic table TIN is above LEAD, the metal of the previous chakra, and with an atomic weight of only 118.7 atomic mass units (amu) it is nearly half of that of LEAD at 207.2 amu.

Before Hahnemann proved Stannum as a remedy it was often used as a vermifuge. Worms in the intestines can certainly cause chronic illness, sometimes severe and debilitating, depending on the type of worms.

The pains of **Stannum Metallicum** 'increase gradually and gradually subside'. Listed in the **Mind** section we have 'sad and discouraged', a 'dread of seeing people', 'very anxious of what others say about her', and 'cannot get rid of an idea once fixed in her mind'. With these symptoms in mind, one can conclude that this is not really someone in control of their destiny, which this chakra is supposed to help create.

It is remarkable that the emotions and sexuality play such prominence with the remedy Stannum, where both <u>males and females can have increased sexual desires</u>, which fit this chakra well. Nevertheless as a 'causation' requiring this remedy it is interesting to note the following: 'ill effects of emotions, fright, dentition, using the voice too much, or causation due to: masturbation'. As long as the last mentioned causation does not lead to a depletion of vital minerals (as well as a weakening of the energetic level of this chakra) by obsessive/compulsive behaviour of this pleasure, then they are not a problem. Otherwise, stock needs to be taken and if the need arises can be addressed with Stannum to lower the sex-drive.

Bowel Nosode – Sycotic Co.

Keynote: Irritability – nervous tension!

The mucous and the synovial membranes are the main focus of this Bowel Nosode, with **catarrhal** conditions in the nose, throat and bronchi, as well as problems within the gastro-intestinal tract and urinary problems. Patients diagnosed with irritable bowel syndrome (IBS) or an irritable bladder (repeated cystitis) are often 'irritable' in every sense of the way themselves, requesting an immediate cure to their ailments! They do not have any patience to 'wait and see' and therefore Syc-co could be the answer in order to calm their nerves; this is particularly effective when taken together with Nux-Vomica.

One of the reasons for the 'irritability' can of course be the **acidity** within the system, called 'acidosis', which is a condition when more acid waste products are in the blood than is normal; this could arise, for example, from increased 'urea' levels due to a lack of alkali in the body, or when the stomach is too acidic. Another reason could be due to having had too many 'vaccinations'! The sacral chakra is the chakra related to the Sycotic Miasm where everything is always 'over the top' and the body cannot cope with too much of anything. As some research of autistic children has suggested vaccines can cause the bowels to be 'irritated'. Another pointer to this Nosode picture is children that suddenly have 'bouts of loose stool'. We should remind ourselves here that the bowels are our second brain and thus the brain will suffer the same fate of 'irritability' as the bowels.

During the night a child may unexpectedly 'wake up with nightmares' (worse between 2-3 A.M.) for no apparent reason and is 'afraid of the dark', as well as 'of animals'. The child may also 'grind teeth during sleep'. 'Food allergies' and 'hay-fever' may develop, and possibly 'asthma' too. Asthma especially may be caused by a vaccine that has been given a few months earlier, although this connection is not always made by the medical profession. In the acute scenario after the vaccine the child might have developed symptoms of **meningitis** (having triggered a miasmatic tendency; see Chapter Three for the connection to the Sycotic Miasm) and can be part of Syc-co, too. In this case, however, a trip to the hospital is always necessary, as no risks should be taken.

Apart from the food allergies the child may become very 'picky' about food, often with a 'diminished' appetite that will make the mother 'irritable' herself. For example they like pizza but 'hate tomatoes' and therefore must have these removed from the pizza. They are not keen on any fruit or vegetables either, with an aggravation from onions. Furthermore as a rule the child will not be too enthusiastic about breakfast. It is not hard to imagine how frustrated the mother will get with a child refusing to eat what she puts in front of him/her. In the worst situation the child refuses to eat at all – and may become anorexic!

With an 'irritable bladder' a child may wet the bed or start wetting again after having been dry for some time. In addition to a restless sleep they also sweat at night, especially on the head. During the day they may 'bite their nails', and could suffer from 'skin problems' like 'dermatitis', 'eczema' or 'ringworm', as well as having 'warts'. As expected with the Sycotic Miasm the two big related remedies are Thuja and Nitric Acid.

One other problem I have found mothers report with Syc-co. is 'more ear-wax' in children than normal. This indicates 'overproduction' in the body, which later in life may be expressed by <u>polyps</u> and <u>cysts</u> in the <u>uterus</u>, as well as genital herpes. Another problem with over-production is 'hair on the face, esp. on the upper lip' for females, arising due to ovarian cysts.

Nervousness associated with this bowel Nosode can be the visible sign of 'twitching of facial muscles' or 'blinking of eyelids', which is easily observed during the consultation. Another sign of this is '<u>restless feet in bed at night</u>' that would need to be asked about.

With all this tension and nervous 'tics' it is no wonder that the patient will feel 'exhausted'. With exhaustion comes frustration and a 'quick temper', and the vicious circle keeps going round and round until Syc-co. and the associated remedies can put a stop to it. Sepia would be a remedy to be given when everything has become 'too much' and the patient cannot 'take anymore', with even the family having become a burden.

One important suggestion here is the use of Mercury 10M to help in detoxification of mercury from 'older' vaccines. (Modern vaccines, we are now assured, do not have this 'nerve-toxin' as an ingredient.) Consequently, the 'neurological-toxin' of vaccinations given previously could be the reason for the twitching, as well as being an indication for this Bowel Nosode, which can also have 'seizures'.

These catarrhal conditions mentioned earlier show how well the metal **Stannum** with '<u>yellow</u> **sputum**' can assist and complement this Bowel Nosode. This 'dampness' within, if not addressed, will later in life lead to 'stiffness all over', 'rheumatism' and 'swellings', for example 'swollen feet at night', or permanent 'nodules on fingers' causing deformities. The stiffness is worse at night and after sitting, but is better for moving, like Rhus-t., which is one of the remedies belonging to this chakra. Unless the above conditions are addressed their personality will remain **'irritable'**.

Remedies related to the Sacral Chakra

Remedies from the Vegetable Kingdom:	**Alf., Card-m., Cham., Chel., China, Cina, Equis., Hydr., Lept., Lyc., Podo, Rhus-t., Nux-v., Puls., Sep., Tarax., Thuj.**
Remedies from the Animal Kingdom:	**Crot-h.**
Remedies from the Mineral Kingdom:	**Ferr-p., Mag-m., Nat-s., Nit-ac., Sil.**
Remedies from the Metal Kingdom:	**Stann., Merc.**

The Nosodes:	**Aids, Bac., Bac-ts., Chlam-t., Herp-s & Herp-z., Maland., Med., Pyrog., Scirr., Tub., Vac., Varicella, Vario., and Syc.co.**
The Sarcodes:	**Chol., Corp-l., Foll., Mamm., Ov., Plac., Prost., Orch., Uter.,**
New Remedies:	**ORANGE** (the colour).
	Rose Quartz – for problems after vaccination.
	Amethyst – daily in low potency can help to calm the adrenals.
	Red Chestnut – to balance the hormones after coming off the Pill or HRT.
	Emerald – also after coming of HRT.
	Bay-leaf – for the spleen and digestive problems, including trouble with the pancreas.

These are just some suggestions for the new remedies we now have from the Guild of Homœopaths.

The SOLAR PLEXUS – No. 3

The SOLAR PLEXUS – belonging to the Mental Body
The Mind – the Personality

Planet: MARS   Element: FIRE   Metal: IRON   Sense: SIGHT

The colour is YELLOW with a wavelength of 570-595 nm

Zodiac: Aries and Scorpio are the Mars Months

Musical note: E = 2 beats/vibrations
Petals 10

This chakra is situated on the spine above the navel and below the level of the shoulder blades. On a subtle level this chakra feeds the stomach and intestines, and when people say they feel a 'knot in their stomach' we can attribute this tightness to blockage of this chakra. **Obsessions** have their seat here including emotional problems such as having a constant fear of making mistakes, but also physical displays like the washing of hands for fear of 'catching something', or being extremely tidy and fastidious, and developing mental tics or strange uncontrollable behaviours.

Primary Organs: LIVER/Gallbladder; its counterpart in the glandular system is the Pancreas

The main focus: self-worth, self-esteem, confidence,
decision-making and personal power.
This chakra motivates the heart.
Tension in this chakra is concerned with Power and Control;
no freedom to be oneself.

The liver, which is the main organ for this chakra, is associated with the emotion **ANGER**. Problems of this chakra will therefore be expressed through trouble with the gallbladder the organ next to the liver, like colic from gallstones, as well as developing tensions in the arteries. Additionally, problems with muscle tone and tendons may arise, such as suffering Dupuytren's Contracture of the hands whereby the flexion of the fingers causes deformity when the hand can no longer be completely straightened, becoming almost a fist! (On an energetic level one may not want to show others the fist? On the other hand, tightness here could be an expression of anxiety and tension.)

High blood-pressure and raised cholesterol levels can certainly be a problem here as well. These aggressions can be expressed by bad temper but also by 'suppressed anger', pointing to remedies like Carcinosin and Staphysagria. The most potent causes for cancer can relate to the dysfunction of the solar plexus. Over-stimulation can lead to various nervous disorders and even hallucinations.

On a personal level the energy of the mental body will manifest itself from age fourteen to twenty-one, helping us to mature into adulthood under the watchful eyes of the parents. Our beliefs and attitudes, which are laid down in childhood, can now be put into practice. Rudolf Steiner used to say that a mother brings a child into this world, but it is the job of the father to 'send the child out into it'. I am quite sure that Rudolf Steiner had this idea from fairy tales, where the father figure sends the child to venture into the world to find 'eternal love and happiness'. Often these fairy tales are found to be similar all around the world, with adventure stories of fighting dragons and finding hidden treasures etc. They are not stories designed to frighten young children but are told to warn them about hidden dangers of their life ahead. It was often the father, or the king representing the father figure, who sends his sons to find their fortunes and/or to prove themselves. In our modern way of life the latter teenage years are the time to take the first hurdle to independence by finishing the basic education, as well as continuing with further studying and making plans for a secure future for oneself.

When this chakra is working well the result will be a 'Warrior' who is not afraid of shying away from life and who undertakes projects with eagerness. On the other hand if this chakra is not working as well as it should, the person will become a 'Servant' or worse a 'Slave' and no longer in charge of their life, merely taking orders. Here, the warrior holding an 'iron' sword and conquering what needs to be overcome is perfect for this picture we are trying to paint; the metal for this chakra is **IRON** and is expressed as a remedy as **Ferrum Metallicum**.

The Planet MARS

Planet Mars belongs to this chakra and represents fire and passion. In mythology Mars was the Roman God of War, yet originally he was the God of Spring, protecting the crops and herds. Mars is the opposite sign to Venus and as we all well know by now 'Men are from Mars, Women are from Venus'! (The title of a 1992 bestselling book by John Gray).

In Chinese Medicine this is the perfect match of **Yin** and **Yang**. On its own, however, Mars carries a lot of masculine energy with a strong willpower and high ambitions, yet can easily be angered and made aggressive, and can be jealous, possessive and impatient.

The planet Mars is cold and desolate and has a less dense atmosphere than that of Earth, yet there must have been a time when the climate was different and recent satellite pictures of Mars show that there are regions of great gorges and canyons where water once flowed. In terms of life on this barren planet, apart from hypothetical inhabitants called 'Martians', there seems to be no life as far as we can tell. (However, this is not to say that spiritual beings do not reside on Mars, as 'The Convoluted Universe' books by Dolores Cannon would have us believe.) In 1898 H.G. Wells wrote 'The War of the Worlds' in which he narrated the fictional horrors of a war between the men of Mars and the dwellers on Earth; let us hope that this remains just fiction!

Astrologically Mars is often looked upon as a bringer of bad luck, which could have been due to its red colour symbolising fire and destruction. But 'out of the ashes rises the Phoenix' is the saying and true enough the word 'phoenix' means 'red fire', and this bird of paradise is linked to '**ascension**' (helping us to understand the saying a little better). Therefore, let us use alchemy homœopathically to help people ascend into the next chakra; the heart. What we are experiencing now globally, and on a collective level, is an elevation of the 'will' into the heart. Because Mars expresses the masculine willpower it can be of assistance here in achieving the next goal by giving strength and preventing being 'faint hearted' about the process.

The Element FIRE

The word **fire** comes from the old English word 'fŷr', which in turn stems from the Greek word for fire 'pur'. Fire symbolises the 'holy spirit' of divine love and the spiritual sun and fire itself provides us with light and the comfort to heat and to cook our food, without which modern society would not exist in the way it does now. The glyph for fire is the upright triangle ▲.

70

Why did the ancient people call this chakra the 'Solar Plexus'? Well, it is linked to the SUN, which is the heart of our planetary system and in turn symbolises our essential self and personality. We can only be transformed by fire; by spiritual fire, the 'spark of life'. A flame is a symbol of the spirit that each one of us carries within. In some people it might be only a flicker while in other it can be like a 'candle shining brightly in the dark', showing others the way. It is the fire within, the love for all creation, which we have to rekindle on a daily basis in order to 'burn brightly'. To love means to give and receive 'fire', but this is not always fully understood as most want to receive more than they want to give, yet it is in the 'giving that we receive', which is one of the laws of the universe. It takes a great deal of knowledge to deliver it correctly.

The flame of a candle creates light, warmth and life; our positive thoughts can merge with the fire, sending them forth with our love. Vigils with lit candles have proved to be a powerful tool within our life-time to show 'unification' of an idea. In unison people gather in peaceful protest, prayers and contemplations, and harmony amongst these people with candles in their hands can hardly be answered with animosities.

We all know that fire burns and we can easily suffer 'burn out' if we burn the 'candle at both ends', as the saying goes. Many illnesses can be caused by this imbalance of love and lack of wisdom. Fire can consume everything and soon nothing but the ashes are left, which is one reason why children should not be allowed to play with matches. Adults, however, often behave like children and 'love playing with fire' (this can also be read as a metaphor for addictions of any sort), sometimes burning out of control; yet a moderate stove keeps the house warm, too. One aspect of the fire element is our metabolism to keep the body warm, aiding digestion in the stomach and the assimilation of food in the small intestine, which is part of this chakra.

The celestial fire, on the other hand, is pure and in Christian tradition the feast of Pentecost celebrates the coming of the Holy Spirit in the form of 'tongues of fire'. This celestial fire will help to keep the oil in the lamps burning. **Fire** represents the male principle of yang and cannot exist if there is no air; the element of the next chakra.

The Colour YELLOW – wavelength 570-595 nm

YELLOW is uplifting in mood. It can help the digestive system and can be used to address liver and gallbladder problems, as we know from the flower remedies such as Chelidonium and Taraxacum (to name just two of the best known ones with yellow flowers). It was said that a 'choleric person' with too much bile in the system needed yellow herbs; for the same reason the colour remedy yellow can clear jaundice in babies.

Yellow encourages laughter and joy and therefore can be a remedy for depression, clearing away negative thinking patterns. It stimulates the lymphatic system and can help with hot flushes at the menopause.

The Metal IRON

The metallic element **IRON** plays a vital part in the body as it is needed to carry oxygen around in the blood, and the remedy **Ferrum Metallicum** proves this point.

If iron is lacking in the blood it is clear that anaemia will arise. Someone who suffers from anaemia will be easily exhausted. They will not want to go out into the world of commerce and generate new business as they 'easily get flushed when having to speak up', have a 'weakness from merely talking or walking', and are 'oversensitive'. This person suffers from 'brain-fag', can be 'irritable', and 'even the slightest noise can be unbearable to them'! While the face flushes easily the skin generally is very pale and delicate, being worse in the winter; a typical anaemic person is a very chilly person indeed. Women in general more likely suffer from anaemia than men, and those who lack a healthy 'blood' will have their menses 'too often and too profuse with labour like pains'.

Young people with anaemia often fall asleep from debility, sometimes even while sitting and studying, yet have sleepless nights with aggravation especially at midnight. With little ambitions this person does not want to be the centre of attention in the workforce or while still studying at university. Not a warrior, more likely a worrier! They have lost the 'iron sword' to conquer 'their' world, be it in commerce, art, or industry, or whatever their special skills happen to be.

Apart from strengthening the blood with iron, for those who feel **uncertainty** these **Bach Flowers Essences** could be of help: **Cerato, Gentian, Gorse, Hornbeam, Scleranthus** and **Wild Oat.**

Bowel Nosode – Morgan Gaertner
Keynote: Allergies

People who are **allergic** to a great variety of food often suffer from excessive flatulence. They might have urgent loose stools, yet constipation is more common. Certainly fatty meals will cause 'distended feelings of the abdomen', possibly with pains coming from the liver/gallbladder. In the worst scenario a gallbladder attack may arise, since gallstones are the norm with cholecystitis (inflammation of the gall-bladder). This patient will have 'eructation of bad odour' and can suffer from 'stomach' as well as 'duodenal ulcers'. As the intestines are 'inflamed' so is the skin, with 'acne rosacea' or 'shingles', both pointing to this remedy.

They 'crave sweets' like most Lycopodium patients, as well as 'salty and hot, spicy food', which will make all the symptoms worse. Any food which **'ferments'** inside the body creates a bigger problem for that person, including skin problems. I have seen this in patients with 'acne rosacea' where a beer in the evening makes the skin 'break out' as revenge the next morning.

Of course there is 'irritability' with all of that, especially between 4-8 P.M. They are 'easily offended' and ask for more beer to calm their nerves! Giving Morgan Gaertner plus Lycopodium, which is one of the big associated remedies in this case, helps to break the cycle of craving the 'wrong food' and becoming less sensitive to other foods that are part of a good diet but which create problems in these patients.

Remedies related to the Solar Plexus

Remedies from the Vegetable Kingdom:	**Acon., Arn., Bell-p., Calen., Chel., Hyper., Crat., Echi., Ham., Lyc., Mill., Nux-v., Plan., Sang., Staph., Symph., Tarax., Urt-u.**
Remedies from the Animal Kingdom:	**Apis, Canth., Scorp.,**
Remedies from the Mineral Kingdom:	**Calc-s., Ferr-p., Kali-c., Kali-p., Nat-m., Nat-s., Hep.,**
Remedies from the Metal Kingdom:	**Ferr., Merc.**
The Nosodes:	**Carc., Cytom.,** (NBWS.-Glandular-fever), **Hepatitis, Morg-Gaert., Parat., Tub-k.**
The Sarcodes:	**Chol., Insulin., Lac-h., Pancreas** and **Pancreatinum, Secret., Pep.** (Proteolytic ferment found in gastric juice).
New Remedies:	**Rice, Chalice Well, Okou., Lumbricus, Ruby, Sandalwood, YELLOW** (the colour).

The HEART CHAKRA – No. 4

The Heart Chakra is connected to the <u>Astral Body</u>
(I feel that one could call it the 'go-between' the lower and upper bodies.)

Planet: SUN   Element: AIR   Metal: GOLD   Sense: TOUCH

The Colour is GREEN with a wavelength of 495-570 nm

Zodiac: Leo is the Sun month *(the opposite is Aquarius)*

The Musical Note is: F = 4 beats/vibrations
Petals 12

The **Heart Chakra is situated between the shoulder blades and the Thymus Gland is its physical counterpart.** This gland is a neglected little gland, yet the **anchoring** of the soul's energy – like the DNA from past lives – has its seat here. To anchor this chakra into the heart would have been detrimental to the physical heart. Thymus Gland in potency can be of great benefit in autoimmune diseases like ulcerative colitis, myasthenia gravis and rheumatoid arthritis to name but a few (see chapter on the Sarcodes). When rejuvenated the thymus gland will become a 'vehicle of ascension'.

The **Heart Chakra is the centre of PROGRESS; our 'home base'. The primary function of this chakra is: LOVE, joy, unity, kinship and peace.** Thus, when this chakra is working well we can be a true **'lover'**, rather than an **'actor' – acting out love** – when there are blockages here.

The energy of LOVE is the cosmic glue, 'serving without causing harm', which was Hahnemann's highest calling to the physician. Love in the relationship with yourself and with others.

The **Organ is the HEART** facilitating a good circulation of the blood.

The Heart Chakra is connected to the 'Astral body', which already is part of our higher mind. In fact we 'explore' this at night-time when we dream. Since most of us have 'forgotten' about our spiritual home this dimension is very much ignored, or at worst laughed about by those who do not understand these realms at all. We will come back to this particular topic later when the remedy potencies are discussed in the conclusions.

As biologists and medics have discovered, the heart is more than just a muscle pumping the blood around the body. It is the body's most important endocrine gland and we also know now that 60 to 65% of the heart's cells are actually neural cells, and not muscle cells as previously believed. Over-stimulation here can cause health problems with the heart; for example, consider the high powered job of an executive running a big company, who tries to do the best for his employees and at the same time has to stay competitive in today's markets. This can put a great burden on the heart chakra and is one reason why heart problems are so common in men doing such jobs with great responsibilities.

The 'Astral body' is the energetic counterpart of this chakra and has traditionally been depicted in old religious paintings as a **halo** or **nimbus** that is <u>placed behind the heads of divine or sacred persons</u> to identify their great dignity. Generally, however, unless you have psychic abilities, this 'halo' around the body cannot be seen. This is changing, however, as modern electronic equipment is able to tune into the frequencies of this electromagnetic field surrounding the body. Consequently I feel that things are getting better, as we grow to be more open to the 'unseen'.

The SUN

The **Sun**, the centre star of our solar system, generates life and vitality without it there would be no life on Earth. Helios was the Greek word for the Sun god: In Greek mythology Helios would climb into his chariot drawn by snow white horses, move across the heaven during the day to bring light, and descend into the ocean in the evening. This source of light and heat was worshipped all around the world: To the Ancient Egyptians it was 'RA', the Aztecs named it 'Tezcatlipoca' (smoking mirror), and the Romans called it either 'SOL' (the Latin word for sun) or 'APOLLO', to name just a few of the most well-known.

In England Druids still gather at Stonehenge on Midsummer's day (the Summer solstice) and on the Winter solstice to greet the sunrise. With the Sun high on the zenith mid-summer was traditionally a good time to get married or to have family celebrations, which of course 'Sunday', the day of rest, is marked for too. The action of the Sun is to shine, enliven, to express and vitalise. If we could be motivated to live through the heart chakra we would all be like the Sun, or son of God, and shine, be inspiring, and have compassion. Generosity, nobility and dignity are words of wisdom here. The Sun is the ruling 'planet' of the zodiac sign LEO, who wants to be very regal and admired and live up to the power and strength the sunlight has.

The Element AIR

Air is not seen, yet is very powerful and always present – it is a mixture of gases in the earth's atmosphere, the main constituents of which are nitrogen, oxygen and argon. It is said that AIR was created when the first element ether began to move, which is ether in action. The glyph of air is the equal sign =, which represents the other two as fire/heaven and water/earth. Air combines and brings about 'movement'. Like the action of breathing in and out, we cannot do just one; there has to be a steady flow of taking it in and letting go again. The dynamics of this is paramount for vitality, allowing oxygen to be carried around the body by the blood.

A homœopath can find a lot of vital clues as to how a person is feeling, merely by observing the way they breathe and talk. If they breathe in a very shallow manner and yawn or sigh a lot this often indicates that 'something' is troubling them, like a heavy burden that is literally sitting on their chest. Alternatively they may talk in an excited way and act 'hyper' in every sense, hardly taking a breath to speak. If such mannerisms are quite prominent then choosing remedies accordingly and selecting some for the heart chakra would certainly not be wrong.

Air is very mobile and even when it is full of noxious fumes it cleanses and renews itself with great speed. The breath of life, the drawing in of air that surrounds us, also means we share it with everyone and all life around us, animals and plants included. Air symbolises communication and intellectual pursuit, as well as new beginnings.

To breathe 'one's last breath' is to die, when we leave our earthy body. Once we have fulfilled our contract of the current life on this planet the four elements have had their turn in events on this physical plane. Thus we can move onto the element ether, which will be considered with the next chakra.

The Colour GREEN – wavelength 495-570 nm

GREEN is positioned between yellow and blue in the colour spectrum, just like the heart chakra is the go-between the lower and the upper chakras. This is reflected in the old tradition of wearing green at medieval weddings; not the colour a modern bride would choose! Some of our new crystal remedies are green, two of which are Emerald and Moldevite. These help us to move on in life and are very empowering. Green is a remedy for harmony and balance. Additionally, green is a heart tonic and can help with fluid retention, as well as inflammations.

The Metal GOLD

As one would expect from this chakra the **metal is Gold** (to have a 'heart of Gold') and the remedy is **Aurum Metallicum**, which we know as a big 'grief' remedy! The grief can result from disappointment in love, the loss of a property, but also from prolonged anxiety over unusual responsibility. For example, this could be if someone matures 'too soon', or is 'too young to have to care for other family members'. The burden of caring for others at an early age could have been too much and may result in 'acute depression' or 'hopelessness'. So gloomy is their mood, in fact, that they may 'talk of committing suicide'.

This could also arise due to pressure from parents to do extremely well at school and thus creating a situation of 'feeling a failure' if the results are not matched to the expectations of the parents. And yet they crave success, are real workaholics, very industrious and ambitious, whilst at the same time can be 'haughty'. They think that their 'salvation is up' and might answer by 'questioning everything'.

There is often chronic insomnia with the depression and lots of bone pains, which are worse at night, as well as 'violent pains in the head' also 'worse during the night'! One might not be too surprised for them wishing to leave it all behind and return to spirit.

Aurum is a very 'syphilitic' remedy with lots of physical heart complaints, such as a 'rapid, feeble, irregular pulse', 'sensations as if the heart has stopped beating', or 'high blood pressure' and arteriosclerosis, as well as angina pectoris.

If gold in potency can put the spark back into people's lives by not only lifting their depression, but also reducing the pains and strengthening their heart, then great strides have been made. They would feel like the Sun, the remedy 'Gold' would bring back the shine and give them a brighter attitude towards their daily interactions with others, consequently bringing back their happiness.

The metal gold is used in the 'band of gold' we use as a wedding ring, yet not pure gold as this would be too soft. It is amalgamated with copper and silver, which are both above gold on the periodic table, giving it more durability, as well as a difference in colouring.

Bowel Nosode – Proteus

Keynote: Brainstorms

'Hysteria' is one of the first impressions you get from this remedy, with sudden brainstorms and the picture that the person 'could commit murder if crossed'. As a child this will be expressed by a 'violent temper, outbursts, kicking and screaming' and possibly rolling on the floor. (A case for the 'super-nanny', if you watch this kind of programme on TV: Homœopaths should get together with these super-nannies to help numerous families to stop such nightmare situations with Proteus and Stramonium, of course!)

One reason why a child might be in this appalling 'state' could be that it suffers from threadworms, with 'rectal spasms'. Like a 'Tubercular child' they may knock their 'heads on the bed or wall'. Apart from the 'destructiveness' they are very 'stubborn' and have 'fixed ideas'. Their circulation is not too good either, with cramps or spasms in the legs, which are icy cold. This cramping can produce headaches, like in Nat-m. and Ignatia, to mention just two of the associated remedies here. A 'broken heart' with grief from disappointed love would certainly call for the above mentioned remedies.

Remedies related to the Heart Chakra

Remedies from the Vegetable Kingdom: **Cact., Crat., Dig., Euph., Helia., Ign., Op., Stram.**

Remedies from the Animal Kingdom: **Apis, Lac-f., Lach., Naja.**

Remedies from the Mineral Kingdom: **Bar-c., Bar-m., Glon., Kali-m., Kali-p., Mag-m., Nat-m., Phos.**

Remedies from the Metal Kingdom: **Aur.**

The Nosodes: **Bac., Bac-ts., Coli.,** (in case of Hypotension), **Med., Prot., Tub., Syph.**

The Sarcodes: **Thym-gl.**

New Remedies: **Adam., Berlin Wall, Buddleja, Chalice Well, Cygnus-c., Emerald, Ether, Frankincense, Green** (the colour), **Holly, Hornbeam, Lotus, Mim-h., Moonstone, Pink, Rose Quartz, Rhodocrosite, Sea Salt, Sol., Salix Fragilis, Tiger Eye** and **Willow.**

The THROAT CHAKRA – No. 5

And the three UPPER BODIES

It is connected to the <u>Etheric Body</u>, which is part of our higher self.

Planet: VENUS   Element: ETHER   Metal: COPPER   Sense: hearing/listening

The Colour is BLUE with a wavelength of 440-495 nm

Zodiac: Libra and Taurus are the Venus Months.

Musical Note: G – 4 beats/vibrations
Petals 16

The **Throat Chakra** is situated at the neck. As an energy centre it affects the **medulla oblongata,** as well as the **carotid gland.** The glands are: **Thyroid and Parathyroid. A good Communicator** will result if this chakra is working well and is free of blockages, while **tension** here relates to wanting to **express oneself, but daring not to do so,** resulting in the **'silent child'**; nervy and not wanting to speak up. Energetically these glands govern the lungs, bronchial and vocal cords.

Primary function: Truth, communication, integrity, willpower and creativity.

The **Throat chakra** could also be called the **'energy transformer'**, as it acts like a satellite dish to receive telepathic messages. Even if we have not developed our psychic abilities fully we can 'receive' blockages in the body through our hands, like in 'Reiki' or 'Cranial Sacral therapy'. In such therapies, when working to facilitate healing, we let our hands be the instrument creating a positive flow. This 'tuning-in' is called 'clairsentience' and the more we give, the more we 'receive'; and as always 'practice makes perfect'. There is certainly nothing 'spooky' about working with your hands as a healer and even people who are totally sceptical will often feel something, sometimes even admitting it willingly. It certainly is a joy to work with patients in this way too, and very humbling when honouring the body with these therapies. Motivation and intentions are part of the plan that we all have to fulfil while on Earth, releasing us from bondage. Thus these next three chakras plus their associated energy bodies will aid in the ascension process.

I would like to add here that if a child has experienced a trauma of any sort, or even an anaesthetic of any length, then this shock can literally get 'stuck in the throat', the symptoms of which might take a lifetime to produce. Thus the child is no longer able to focus on its 'life mission', almost as if it has lost its way. The fairy tale of Hansel and Gretel comes to mind here: The children get lost when out walking in the woods and cannot find their way home. They almost starve to death and eventually end up in the house of a witch! I always like to compare the Thyroid and Parathyroid with the story of Hansel and Gretel; if these glands are not working well in younger years the child will not 'thrive', and just like Hansel and Gretel, will lose their way in life. Not only will respiratory problems like asthma result from a trauma here, but menstruation irregularities in girls with anaemia and fatigue are common.

Since the throat is like a 'bottle-neck' in the body, if the thyroid and parathyroid glands do not function fully then a child will not grow as it should (maybe even growing fat, which is the opposite side of this coin, although still very much a thyroid problem), as we shall see later when we look at the Sarcodes. The Throat Chakra is the opposite of the Solar Plexus, where the keynote of Morgan-Gaertner is 'allergies'. The same applies here, with allergies like 'hay-fever', as well as 'asthma' and recurring bronchitis, needing to be treated via this chakra, with Carcinosin, Tuberculinum and Bacillinum being high on the list of related Nosodes.

The Planet VENUS

Venus is the brightest of all the planets and orbits between Mercury and Earth. It has an atmospheric pressure 100 times that of Earth and an average surface temperature of 500 degrees Celsius and thus is not very 'inviting' for humans to pay a visit to. In Greek mythology the planet Venus was also called Aphrodite and was the ruler of love, marriage and fashion: More information on Venus is found under the Zodiac sign of Libra.

The Element ETHER

Ether (or Aether) was classically considered to be the 'space' between every living cell, the space everywhere where there is no matter, and the space of 'outer space'. The glyph of ether is the circle O, where everything comes from the centre. The Hindu word for ether or space is 'Akasha', which equally is the Sanskrit word for 'luminous essence'. It also represents esoteric teaching, where all knowledge – past, present and future – is held in form of the 'Akashic Record'. This record can also be called the 'Collective Consciousness', where all human experiences are stored in the psychic realms that are shared by everyone; if we could 'see' or 'read' this ether containing our thoughts then I am sure we would be a lot more careful of what we wish for!

Aristotle, who argued that nature abhorred a vacuum, called ether the 'fifth element' or the 'quintessence', yet in modern physics we have nothing directly analogous to this. In a vacuum only electromagnetic energy is measurable and therefore we could compared ether with the modern terms used to describe fields in such a void: 'Free space', 'Planck's particles', 'quantum foam', and 'quantum wave state'. Maybe the 'zero point field' discussed earlier could also be part of this expression of energy not seen? In Homœopathy we work with dilutions beyond our comprehension and from a chemical point of view the remedies cannot possibly work! Yet we know that they do, and millions of patients can testify to this from the help that they have received via the sugar globules 'with nothing in them'. Thus let us believe that the ether we cannot see, smell or touch does exist as philosophers have taught us throughout the ages.

The Colour BLUE – wavelength 440-495 nm

BLUE is the vehicle you use to get back to your true self. It is the link between spirit and matter! This remedy is close to Dolphin, which is another remedy that gives visions of our spiritual home and being the centre to 'voice' opinions it will help us to express ideas. Consequently if this centre is blocked by sore throats, constant catarrh, and a tired voice it will help to cool inflammations and strengthen the voice box. It will also help to stop 'addictions' of any sort as it prevents us from being hooked continually on the same 'idea' (compulsive behaviour). (This remedy is especially good for people who like to gossip.) The remedy Blue helps us to disconnect and therefore to shed negative habits and thoughts. It symbolises harmony and truth and helps to soothe and calm the mind.

The throat centre is also the place of temptation; it is here where we fall into pride and we must learn not to take a downward path again, which can be achieved by developing the spiritual centres. It is the gland that is most affected by radiation and the remedy Blue can help to clear this!

The Metal COPPER

The **metal Copper** is a wonderful conductor of both heat and electricity and thus is often used in heating appliances and in electronic equipment. Copper as a remedy is called **Cuprum Metallicum**. It very much affects the nervous system causing spasmodic effects, convulsions and cramps: These can be in the fingers, toes, calves and soles of the feet, as well as causing clenching of thumbs in the palms, clonic spasms and epilepsy. In the stomach 'hiccoughs precede the spasms'. They might suffer 'periodic attacks of vomiting' while another symptom from the proving picture is that 'when drinking fluid it descends with gurgling sounds'. The patient can be **hypersensitive to every drug,** over-reacting without curing. (Others remedies to use for the same reason are Carcinosin and Mercury, as well as Med. and Ph-ac.).

People needing copper in potency often suffer from over-sensitivity: For some individuals 'getting their feet wet causes an epileptic fit', whereas others endure 'ailments from emotions, anger, fright, suppression, and are overworked mentally or physically, with ill effects of loss of sleep'. They are indeed 'fearful' and shun everybody, with a 'fear of society' and bouts of violent weeping, yet on the other hand may demonstrate 'convulsive laughter' just like the picture of Thyroidinum with 'laughing in a way peculiar to her'. These individuals can be malicious and morose, using words unintentionally and giving 'piercing shrieks'.

The throat chakra may be the chakra for communication but 'shrieking' is not exactly the right way to go about it. In fact they can bite, beat and tear things and like to 'imitate and mimic', which reminds me of autistic children I have treated. In one particular case both parents had a problem with their thyroid and this weakness was passed on to one of their children, a boy who developed severe autistic tendencies after a vaccine given at the age of two. This vaccine was, if you like, the 'straw which broke the camel's back'. On its own, without the inherited weakness of the thyroid on both side of the family, the child could have been fine. At worse he would have been only slightly autistic, maybe suffering from Asperger Syndrome, rather than severe autism where the spectrum of symptoms can vary greatly. Being a 'chronic' problem this can be a life-long challenge to the parents, as well as the homœopath. Parents often give up too easily and try homœopathy for only a short time, feeling that the impact is not great enough to carry on with it. However, remedies can help, especially when giving the Bowel Nosodes, starting with the base chakra.

People needing Cuprum are most likely to have a pale bluish facial colour, with blue lips that are sunken and pinched. (This can also be observed in children suffering from epilepsy.) The skin is reported to have severe itching but without any eruptions, which all points to the over-sensitivity of the nerves. It is clear to see why someone needing this remedy turns out to be the negative archetype of the silent child. If this could have been balanced right from the start with the right remedy in the required potency then a good communicator with stimulating conversations would have been the result.

Bowel Nosode – Gaertner

Keynote: the Children's Nosode and malnutrition

In medical terminology **'Ketosis'** is mentioned in conjunction with this Nosode for children. Ketosis describes a state where a ketone molecule (such as acetone) accumulates in the tissue, which can arise from a late complication of **juvenile diabetes mellitus**. Acetone is a substance that smells like nail polish remover (since acetone is the active ingredient in this cosmetic product) and is usually not present in high concentrations in the body, but forms at elevated levels in the body after vomiting or during diabetes. It is also found in high amounts in urine during conditions of 'starvation' (starving the body of vital nutrients due to the wrong bowel flora). Large quantities of these acid compounds in diabetes indicate an approaching coma.

Acetonuria, as the name suggests, is acetone found in urine and gives off a sweet smell. Might this be the reason why children with ketosis who need this Bowel Nosode are 'not thriving'? Despite being an 'intelligent' child, they are a 'bit nervous' and 'sensitive to all impressions' since they have an **'undernourished'** body.

One problem why these patients are not putting on weight could be coeliac disease. Before resorting to a very strict diet of no gluten at all it would be useful to try Gaertner. These digestive problems can start very early in life with the child vomiting everything. In the past coeliac disease was often not recognised early enough for children to benefit from a change in their diet. One of the symptoms of coeliac disease, apart from looking pale and skinny is a frequent 'frothy and offensive stool'. Remember, the stool is just what we are looking at when thinking of the bowel flora and the Nosodes. Silicea as a remedy certainly springs to mind when thinking of a 'pale child', looks delicate and does not grow as expected. Without a doubt Silicea is one of the associated remedies to be considered here.

These children can have night terrors and want to sleep next to their mother (like Pulsatilla); they often want the light on, too, and are late in falling asleep and might even sleep-walk. Gaertner can stop teething problems in babies when Chamomilla has failed to help. It will also help to stop the discharge from the ears every time they cut a tooth.

Remedies like Calc-Carb or any other Calcium related remedy like Calc-p. and Calc-f. are very much needed for this chakra too, since all these are related to the thyroid. Phosphoric remedies are equally useful, as suggested earlier. Thus, for children failing to blossom help is at hand with Gaertner and the dozens of remedies, old and new, in our homœopathic tool kit.

Remedies related to the Throat Chakra

Remedies from the Vegetable Kingdom:	**Berb., Caul., Cham., Equis., Fuc., Petros., Phyt., Puls., Sabal, Sars., Solid., Staph., Thuj.**
Remedies from the Animal Kingdom:	**Ambra., Apis, Bufo, Lach., Sep., Spon.,**
Remedies from the Mineral Kingdom:	**Bar-p., Bar-s., Benz-ac., Calc-c., Calc-f., Calc-i., Calc-p., Calc-Sil., Kali-p., Nat-m., Nat-p., Nat-s., Phos., Zinc-p.**
Remedies from the Metal Kingdom:	**Cupr., Merc.**
The Nosodes:	**Anas-b., Bac., Carc., Gaert., Med., Strept., Syph., Tub.,**
The Sarcodes:	**Thyr., Parath.,** and **Calcitonin** (helping to regulate the calcium in the body).
New Remedies:	**Blue and Pink** (the colours) and **Turquoise. Berlin Wall, Buddleia, Copper Beech, Goldfish, Lac-h., Moldevite, Plut., Sequoia and Sycamore Seed.**

The BROW CHAKRA – No. 6

Planet: and Metal MERCURY   Sense: Inner Sound – the soul is ready to receive messages
The Colour is Indigo with a wavelength of 410-440 nm
Zodiac: Gemini and Virgo are the Mercury Months
Musical Note: A = 4 beats/vibrations
Petals 96

The **Brow Chakra** is located in the **centre of the forehead; also called the Third EYE.**
The centre is governed by the Pineal Gland:
Here we find the Buddhic Body or the AWARENESS Body
If tension is felt here: You are not allowed to be who you are, you just play a 'role'.

**Primary function: Wisdom, knowledge, intuition, discernment and imagination
– information for happiness and health.**

The Brow Chakra motivates integration (integrity) and inner vision, with intuition and clairvoyance taking place if working well. The **Intellectual**, on the other hand, needs everything to be in black and white, and lacks 'insight'; as Neal Donald Walsch so aptly said in his book 'Conversation with God': "If you do not go within – you go without!"

Through this chakra our belief systems can influence our own healing, as is well demonstrated by the placebo effect. People can get better simply because they believe that the medicine they have taken in a trial run was the 'real' one; the belief alone can work the magic. This is one reason why medical doctors, who are not familiar with Homœopathy (that it is an 'energy-medicine' and has the ability to change things from within), might argue that the only way in which it works is by the 'placebo' effect. Well, anyone who ever took a Belladonna when it was not needed and 'proved' it by getting very hot, possibly suddenly having a headache too, will be surprised by the effect of that little 'sugar pill'. And of course people who have given globules to their children or pets (who do not know what they are getting and what it is good for) are equally surprised how quickly the remedies worked.

I would like to mention a little case scenario here, where a patient's wife phoned me late one afternoon after her husband had injured his eye while working, **but did not want to see the doctor** (after an eye injury I always advise that it must be seen by a medical doctor). I directed her to give him an **Arnica** from her first aid kit and phone for a taxi at the same time. This was done and as soon as her husband had taken the Arnica he said: 'I think, I'd better go to hospital and have the eye checked out!' His wife just laughed and said: 'That is exactly what Doris said, that you would want to see the doctor after taking the Arnica, so I have ordered the taxi already!' The husband could not believe that I had forecast his request to see the doctor after all, but if you know the picture of Arnica and know that the patient 'does not want to see the doctor or nurse', you can see how his energy changed immediately after the Arnica 30c; it made him realise that it was better the eye was seen to. Homœopathy is an energy medicine and by giving him back the energy that was lacking due to the shock and pain caused from his injury, he was again 'in tune' with his 'higher self' and requested to see the doctor. As it turned out no great damage had occurred to the eye, which was bloodshot from the injury but otherwise fine.

The Colour INDIGO– wavelength 410-440 nm

Indigo is a dark blue colour and this remedy can act as a sedative; a tonic for the overused mind for people who analyse everything and gives clarity to unsolved problems. Indigo fosters intuition and spirituality. It has also been found helpful with dyslexia and has helped to clear headaches.

The Planet and the Metal MERCURY

MERCURY the Planet and **Mercury** the **METAL** is the next focus. The Planet Mercury is the closest planet in our Solar System to the Sun and takes only 88 days to circulate it. To the Romans Mercury was the 'winged messenger' of the gods carrying the CADUCEUS. The caduceus is nowadays the general symbol for doctors, pharmacists and healers. The wand represents the spine and the two serpents intertwined around it and crossing over at the chakras in turn represent the two nervous systems, starting at the base of the spine and meeting at the head. Traditionally Mercury ruled communication, which of course the third eye is associated with, putting us in touch with God. With this sense of the 'Inner Vision/Sound', are we ready to see and hear?

Mercury Vivus, the **Quicksilver** as the remedy:

Mercury is the only metallic element that is liquid at room temperature and anyone who has dropped the old fashioned type mercury thermometer knows that uncontained the mercury will 'scatter' everywhere as tiny 'pellets'. This liquid mercury gives off a toxic vapour that is highly volatile. Inhaling the vapour can lead to poisoning of internal organs, especially the **brain** and **kidneys**. Exposure to mercury vapour might occur from having to work with it in industry, where it is often an ingredient found in some paints, cosmetics products and pesticides. Another more frequently occurring exposure to mercury is from the amalgam used in dentistry to fill our teeth!

As a remedy Mercury is known as the '**human thermometer**', affecting almost every organ in the body, and is very much related to the syphilitic miasm. Its remedy picture illustrates someone with 'poor self-confidence', 'changing their minds all the time' and with an 'uncontrollable desire to travel far away' like the tiny mercury pellets when they scatter. The person has the sensation that they 'must move' and 'cannot find the right place', thus you had better catch them while you can and give them a dose of mercury in potency to stabilise this 'constant suffering' and 'internal turmoil'. Like a 'thermometer' they are very 'sensitive to hot and cold', being worse at night with 'profuse nightly sweating'. All pains are worse from the 'warmth of bed'; nevertheless they can also suffer 'creeping chilliness'. The picture of Mercury with its 'foul smelling discharges' is not a pretty one. We can see how its toxicity can hinder us in moving into the crown chakra to become wiser.

Like the toxic picture of mercury poisoning with tiredness, tremors, poor coordination, numbness of limbs, impairment of vision, kidney failure (severe poisoning is fatal) and occasionally dementia, the remedy picture confirms the tremors in Parkinson's disease, which so often commences with trembling of the hand as the first sign. Internal toxicity of this sort increases the flow of saliva, staining the pillow, as well as giving 'spongy gums', a 'sweet metallic taste', and 'halitosis'.

Halitosis reminds me of a case of a gentleman in his late 40s where the wife asked me for help. Her husband's bad breath was so noticeable that she felt the need to air the room every time he left for work in the morning. She wanted to help him, as she was embarrassed for the people he had to work with who 'suffered' on his behalf. When I visited them in Germany the first thing I noticed when entering their house were 'guns' (old collector's pieces) hanging on the walls in the hallway, 'welcoming the visitor'. I just could not help making a comment about these numerous pieces to his wife, who replied that she hated her husband's 'fetish' about these 'murderous weapons'. (For me it just confirmed the strong syphilitic background inherited by their son (from his father), who had scoliosis of the spine and numerous health problems ever since he was born.) When she requested remedies for her husband I addressed it with Mercury and the miasm accordingly, which worked like a charm on the halitosis. Not having taken a full case history at the time I treated him successfully with Mercury in potency for his very bad breath, which was the only problem at the time.

Bowel Nosode – Dysentery Co.

Keynote: NERVES and Anticipation

According to the books this Bowel Nosode had a conventional proving in 1929 and it is said that it 'affects every tissue in the body', like Mercury the metal. Since it is associated with nervous tension this statement is of course very plausible. The nervousness can start even in a young child, being very anxious in the morning before school and having loose stools before leaving the house. With **'diarrhoea on excitement and worry'** they can very often pass stool, up to 5-6 times a day (with IBS even more often).

These children are 'hypersensitive' and stammer with excitement. At school the teacher might complain that they are 'restless' and 'fidgety' with a desire to wander around in the classroom. Twitching of the face and eyelids might be observed. These children might also suffer from recurring tonsillitis and hay-fever: Not a happy child, being so anxious, with a **'lack of self-confidence'** and **'easily flustered'**.

Like Argentum Nitricum they crave sweet, sugary food, cakes etc., which worsens their bowel problem as well as the headaches they often suffer from, too. These people suffer terrible **migraines** (including vomiting) on a regular basis, often with a **periodicity every 7 to 14** days (like Arsenicum Album., which is one of the associated remedies). Included in this picture are 'blinding headache with loose bowels' as a result of 'nerves', the **pylorus** going into **'spasm'** for the same reason, or **duodenal ulcers** and lots of **heartburn** some hours after food. This nervous tension can even cause **tachycardia** and **palpitation** with extra systolic beats, and this irregular heartbeat makes the already tense person even more worried. By giving them Dys-Co. to relieve them of the fear of suffering a heart attack, it helps them to relax enough to bring down their blood pressure.

From my observations, when the blood pressure is slightly raised I give Dys-Co. 200c as a split dose (two doses of the same remedy given within 24 hours) once a month and find it works exceedingly well. Usually no other medication is needed providing the patient is not overweight, which of course they might be due to their love of sweet food which adds to their problems. At the same token by giving Dys-Co. their hunger for snacking on cakes and chocolate bars are greatly reduced, thus helping to reduce the weight as well, which in itself can reduce high blood pressure.

People needing Dys-Co. are always 'in a hurry' and are 'full of worries', which causes **'hot flushes'** during the menopause as well as **insomnia** from 'crowding thoughts'. Whilst falling asleep they can have 'sudden shocks through the body', resulting in being fully awake again or **waking up at 2-3 A.M.**; both strong pointers to this Nosode. In fact they might wake up at 3 A.M. and are not able to go back to sleep until 6 A.M., which means that they fall asleep shortly before it is time to get up. Consequently they are exhausted from the very moment they get up; as a result another day full of worries about how they will cope is to follow?

Their dreams are not pleasant either, being very vivid with very real burglars, fire or dead people, or falling from a 'height'. In the morning generally they do not feel like eating breakfast due to their nervousness. Some will leave the house and just have a coffee on the way to the office, which is so often observed when living in the city these days. For other patients the coffee would be far too strong for their 'delicate' nerves; it would just cause them yet another headache or migraine. One observation I have also made with these patients is that they 'worry about taking remedies' in case their symptoms might get worse. Arsenicum Album, which is one of the leading remedies here of course, has this problem in common. It is easy to see here how 'fearful' they are and how much they worry about everything.

The older they get the more 'mentally exhausted' they are and the 'poorer the memory'. Since mercury is a nerve toxin and is the metal for this chakra I am sure you can see how these two remedies can also complement each other, as well as Nux Vomica for 'nerves' and for 'being in a hurry', or Lycopodium as well as Argentum Nitricum for the 'sweet tooth' and the anticipation these patient suffer from excessively.

Remedies related to the Third Eye

Remedies from the Vegetable Kingdom:	**Anac., Dros., Cham., Ign., Lob., Lyc., Spong., Nux-v., Verat.**
Remedies from the Animal Kingdom:	**Tarent.**
Remedies from the Mineral Kingdom:	**Ant-t., Arg.-n., Cadm-s., Cinnb., Kali-m., Kali-p.**
Remedies from the Metal Kingdom:	**Ars., Arg., Merc.**

The Nosodes: **Bac., Cand-a., Dys-co,. Prot., Tub.**

The Sarcodes: **Hypoth., Melant., Pineal, Serot.**

New Remedies: **Amethyst, Ash, Goldfish, Indigo** (the colour) **Hornbeam, Lotus, Purple** (the colour), **Ruby, Salix Frag.,** and **Stonehenge.**

The CROWN CHAKRA – No. 7

Planet: MOON   Metal: SILVER

The Colour is Purple with a wavelength of 380-410 nm

Zodiac: Cancer is the Moon Month

Musical note: B = 2 beats/vibrations
Petals 972

The **Crown Chakra** is situated above the head and the relating gland is the **Pituitary Gland**, which is the master gland that manages the activities of the thyroid, parathyroid, pancreas, gonads and the adrenal glands. (Here the Silver Cord is the link between the physical body and the subtle energy bodies.)

Tension here is due to '**Authority**' – you want to feel separate, but you are not able to do so. Here we should have our highest spiritual awareness. It is pivotal in accessing our true potential – the beginning of the **Monad** (a simple invisible unit; one of the primary elements of being).

The Spirit is connected to the Pituitary gland and is associated with the '**Causal Body**', which is the deepest part of consciousness; the home of GOD, or 'all that is', within our deepest desires/goals. **Primary function: Beauty, spirituality, and connection with the Divine.**

The '**Guru**', who can teach others, is the positive functioning and the more developed this centre is the greater and brighter will be the aura. In contrast, the **Egoist** – who is totally self-centred and selfish – is the opposing side of this coin.

The Colour PURPLE– wavelength 380-410 nm

PURPLE the remedy strengthens and calms the mind and enhances the immune system (like Echinacea has a purple flower). It was always chosen as the 'royal' colour or for religious leaders in high office. If stressed from the burden of a high powered job the remedy Purple will help to calm down the adrenal glands and for this reason can be given in low potency for weeks, or even months.

The flower Lavender, with its purple flower head, is well known for its soothing effect and helping to sleep. Do not to forget Pulsatilla here, its 'other' name being 'Pasque' flower, which is the French name for Easter; in the Christian calendar this is the time for resurrection from the dead. This flower also has a purple bloom and carries this vibration within, helping to bring about <u>changes</u> in peoples' lives.

Purple eases their egoistical streak and can even help them with a drug addiction: Remember that Prof. Popp found that a **wavelength of 380 nm was the most efficient in 'photon-repair' of the cells.** As it is associated with the crown it is also connected to psychic powers.

The MOON

The Moon, Earth's only satellite, has always held great fascination and the lunar calendar of 28 days proves influential to people in a variety of ways. Like the ebb and tide of the World's oceans, some people suffer mentally, being more unstable during a full moon or sometimes sleeping badly or even not at all. The moon is also called the 'Queen of the night', representing our unconscious that is not so readily seen, yet is present all the same. Each year in Japan the Moon has a birthday on 15th September to celebrate **YIN**, the feminine embodiment of chi (while Yang, the opposite, expresses the male aspect of the Universe).

The night light bathing the Earth in a 'silvery' glow not only adds mystery, but gives us a clue to the remedy for this chakra called LUNA, which is moonlight in potency. From clinical experience we are told that this remedy has worked for insomnia, nightmares and sleep-walking. As one would expect it also helped with 'female disorders', like 'menses irregular' and 'inter-menstrual flow'. Others have reported that 'headaches', acidity and oedema of the face (moon-face), neck and hands have been cured by giving Luna.

Some health problems are known to be worse during times of full moon. One example is worm infestations, which can be successfully addressed with Luna. Another condition worse during full moon is skin problems, which can equally be treated with Luna or remedies like Alum., Calc., Graph., Nat-m., Sil., and Sulph., which are listed as 'base chakra' remedies. However, those remedies needed 'below' are also required 'above', as this is the opposite end of the same yardstick.

Finally, coming back to the planet MOON, the dream of putting a man on the Moon in the last century in the end became reality; this notion was no longer just a children's story of 'the man in the moon', as told when I was young.

The Metal SILVER

The metal **Silver** is linked not only to the chakra but to **Luna**, the **Moon**. **Argentum Metallicum** is **silver in potency**. The picture of this remedy declares that there is 'loss over mind and body, and loss of mental power'. The person is a **hypochondriac**, with 'anxiety about health', 'neurosis from worries', and 'maniacal' and in a 'depressive state', going into 'pre-senile' or 'senile dementia'. The crown chakra is totally blocked. This can start even in children with 'nightly fears', crying for a long time about trifles, weary, sad, and in a pitiful state.

Argentum Metallicum **thickens the tissue**, especially the cartilages when suffering from so-called 'hysterical joints'. If this thickening happens to be in or around the head it can lead to 'exotosis of the skull' and benign bone tumours. Yet these people have a delusion of a 'head that feels empty and hollow': Some kind of anomaly, you must admit!

The 'want for sweets' is **not** as great as in Argentum Nitricum, but the appetite is very much increased and they are 'hungry after eating a full meal'. The patient is so 'hungry in the morning, that it gives them nausea' (hypoglycaemia) and this 'nausea can even occur in dreams'. In fact the sleep can be disturbed by 'terrifying dreams', which leaves the person worried when waking. The subconscious is playing 'real tricks', as dreams have their own interpretations. One such analysis of nausea in dreams is 'throwing up indigestible thoughts or feelings' and 'sickening emotions', which begs the question: what is the person trying to get rid of? A lot of soul-searching to this question might be the answer here, as well as giving Argentum Metallicum to open up the way to the crown chakra.

Bowel Nosodes – Bac. No. 7 and No. 10

Keynote: 'Fatigue' and premature senility.

These two Nosodes are just given numbers because Bach and Paterson 'ran out of ideas for names'. They too, however, are non-lactose fermenting type of bacillus when they were cultured on a Petri dish. The 'mental and physical fatigue' is mentioned more for Bacillus No. 7, rather than No. 10.

This kind of exhaustion is not expected in a young person, yet I have had a teenager where the mother reported that the 'neck cracked' (like a nut) when the head was turned and the limbs were stiff, in particular the knee. This came about due to too much exercise for competition sport and now exhaustion was the problem. Bac. No. 7 was not the only answer here; the sports training was stopped (as the doctor had requested this too) and this helped her to focus again on her school work, which had become a real problem as well – due to exhaustion. **Not being able to focus on mental work**, the mere thought of which causes aggravation, is another indication.

Often there is myocardial weakness, **low blood pressure** and a **slow pulse**! Sleep can be a great problem too, with waking at 2 or 3 A.M. and taking hours to fall asleep.

The '**cracking of the neck**' is one clue for this remedy and 'not wanting to have breakfast' can be another. In an elderly patient we have osteoarthritis and problems with gout, as well as rheumatoid arthritis with a tendency to 'rheumatic nodules'.

Bac. No. 7 goes well with **Bromide** and **Iodine**, often in conjunction with the **Kali group** (Potassium), i.e. Kali-bromide or Kali-iodatum. **Bac. No. 10** is over-anxious and depressed, with an overactive mind.

Apart from craving sweets and chocolates, and fried fish (not all at the same time I hope) these patients have an aversion to breakfast and can even become **anorexic**; this is similar to those needing Dys-co., the previous Bowel Nosode for the third eye.

A bit unusual are the 'fatty cysts' on the neck, as well as lipoma on lower rib. And although the bowels move first thing in the morning, it is said to be 'sluggish'. A small number of remedies are related here, but nothing stands out except Pic-ac, which shows the 'exhausted' state that they have succumbed to due to their 'overactive mind' being unable to relax and yet equally unable to carry on in the same way. This is where these Bowel Nosodes can break the cycle of repetition, removing the blockage and allowing the person to move on in life to a better place of health.

One last word about 'parasites' and 'worms', which at first sight seems a bit strange for the Crown chakra. But here again we are dealing with 'as above so below' and we see that the remedy we ought to consider here is the Nosode 'Candida albicans'. This is the fungus that is associated with digestive problems and patients that generally 'desire sweets' (that aggravate all their symptoms). We can understand how an unhealthy gut will influence the brain and the proverb that '**it is a bad soil where no flowers grow**' makes sense to any keen gardener, and this may equally be applied in relation to an unhealthy gut affecting a blossoming brain.

However, not only those with green fingers know what parasites can do to flowers; they can eat the roots of the plant and the whole plant withers in front of your eyes within days. Now think of what destruction a parasite can cause inside the body when the body plays 'host' to these unwanted guests. In the terminology of a youngster they are called 'gatecrashers'; not invited to 'this party'!

There are more Chakras above the Crown and one of those is the SOUL STAR – the need to accept the divine equality. However, I will restrict the remedies and associated chakras to the seven main ones.

Remedies related to the Crown Chakra

Remedies from the Vegetable Kingdom:	Anac., Aven., Cina, Cocc., Con., Gink., Hell., Hyos., Ip., Lact., Nux-m., Op., Passi., Spig., Stram., Teucr., Valerian.
Remedies from the Animal Kingdom:	Lac-c., Lyss., Sep.,
Remedies from the Mineral Kingdom:	Arg-n., Ars-i., Calc-i., Ferr-i., Kali-i., Kali-p., Nat-i., Merc-i-f., Phos., Pic-ac.
Remedies from the Metal Kingdom:	Arg.
Remedies from 'Gas':	Brom., Oxyg.

The Nosodes: Bac.no.7 & Bac. no. 10, Cand-a., <u>Carc.</u>

The Sarcodes: Pitu-gland., Pituin.,

New Remedies: Ayahuasca, Blue, Chalice Well, Clay, Cotton, Holly, Lotus, Lumbricus, Luna, Moonstone, Purple (the colour), Rainbow, Sea Holly, Sea Salt and Spectrolite.

Chapter SIX

SARCODES and the GLANDS

Introduction to the Sarcodes

The word **Sarcode** refers to a homœopathic remedy that is made from **healthy animal** or **human tissue or secretions**, such as Thyroidinum, for example, which is a thyroid gland extract, or Iodothyrinum, made from the iodine released by this gland. These extracts in potency are equally called 'organ therapy' remedies. In contrast to the Sarcodes, Nosodes are remedies that have been produced from diseased tissue; for example, Scirrhinum is made from a cancerous growth of the liver and along with other Nosodes can be used very successfully to treat a cancer of the liver.

In homœopathic treatment Sarcodes are nothing new but are not so common and have sometimes been dismissed by practitioners due to a lack of a conventional remedy proving. It is often argues that prescribing these remedies is an easy choice, rather than having to find the 'Simillimum'. On the other hand, however, I feel that the Sarcodes can be used in a similar manner to the Polychrests, acting on a variety of different areas of the body at once. (For those of you who are not familiar with the term Polychrests, this means a remedy with a 'broad spectrum of action'.) Nevertheless, these remedies are not supposed to be looked at as a panacea, i.e. the 'cure-all'.

A Polychrest normally affects all tissues of the patient's body to some degree. Of course, when we talk about the glands and their secretions, we are all affected by the HORMONES they release. The question is just how well are they functioning in the patient?

The word 'Hormone' comes from Greek word 'excite' and that is exactly what hormones do – they excite the body into action. Imagine being chased by a tiger; the adrenal glands would 'kick in' and you would run for your life, faster than you ever thought possible. Or when 'falling in love', we all know what kind of positive effect that has on us; we are happy, have 'pink spectacles' on, and feel 'on top of the world'! It is just a great pity that these feelings do not last very long in most cases.

All the glands in the body are associated with the different chakras and therefore we can treat them by looking at which chakra is either blocked or needs supporting. We can unlock the affected chakra with the Bowel Nosodes and then nurture it with the glandular remedy, plus give a constitutional remedy to bring everything back into balance.

Let us now consider the different glands in the body, starting at the top with the Pituitary Gland. Note here that although we are starting at the top in terms of the glands this is actually in the opposite direction of the Bowel Nosodes and the Chakras, where the Base Chakra is naturally the first one. However, it seems right to start at the other end since the **Pituitary Gland** is the **'Master Gland'**.

The PITUITARY GLAND:

Pituitary Gland
— The <u>Conductor of the endocrine orchestra</u> —
spiritually called the **ENERGY CENTRE OF FAITH.**
The Psychic Sense for this gland would be Clairvoyance.

The quality here would be: perception of <u>inner space</u>, <u>personal ethics</u>, <u>morality</u> and <u>spiritual law</u>. Self-expression is through visual arts, paintings, colours, film and photography.

The first proving of 'Pituitary Gland' as a remedy was conducted by the Proving Committee of Constantine Hering (1800-1880) in 1935. Although this is clearly not a new remedy we now have additional information from the clinical use of the remedy. Incidentally, Hering was the first Homœopath to suggest using the 'saliva of a rabid dog' and 'smallpox scabs' in potency to be given to people suffering from these diseases and thus the 'isopathic movement' was born. It is very fitting here to mention that Hering gave us the great and detailed proving of Lachesis after trying it on himself in many different potencies. He also realised at the age of eighty that Glonoinum (nitro-glycerine) is an excellent 'heart remedy'. Sadly, though, he died of a heart attack shortly after this discovery.

The Pituitary Gland is responsible for the whole of the CHEMISTRY of the body, affecting every cell membrane. It is accountable for <u>growth, metabolic rate</u>, <u>water and electrolyte balance</u>, <u>kidney filtration</u>, <u>ovulation and lactation</u>. This little 'pea-sized' gland, situated behind the nose cavity in the hollow of the central bone at the base of the skull (sphenoid bone), responds to hormones released by the hypothalamus, which monitors the level of the hormones in the blood and is the physical link between the nervous system (movement, sensation and mental activity) and the endocrine system (the metabolism, growth and regulatory processes of the body). Quite a tall order for this tiny gland, so let us take a detailed look at when it could be used beneficially in potency:

It affects growth patterns in children (who are not thriving) and thus we can use it if there is DELAYED PUBERTY.

If in imbalance in adults we can have: **Impotence in males** (with 'fear of impotence'), or prostatitis, in which case 'prostate' in potency can also be considered.

In Females irregularities will be expressed through:

⊚ **Amenorrhea**, or late menses with a cycle of more than 30 days, or scanty.
⊚ **Dysmenorrhoea** – awful cramping, especially a day before or on the first day of menses.
⊚ **Migraine** – especially during menses.
⊚ **Breast disorder**. Amenorrhea with breast atrophy.
⊚ **Infertility** – usually the female is very slight/slim/underdeveloped.
⊚ **Miscarriages**, a history of.
⊚ **Labour:** during, to speed up the process – works wonders. Especially if there is **inertia during the 2nd stage**, where the os is fully dilated. **Kali-p. 200c** hourly should be given too, to help the mother to prevent her from getting exhausted.

Once the **baby** has arrived, if there is projectile vomiting, which may indicate an obstruction of the bowels and is very dangerous, this remedy can be tried before an operation is performed.

Pituitary 200c = never been well since **(NBWS)** <u>induced birth</u>, either for mother or child, or both.

Pituitary and Thyroid Gland in potency are both listed for children with Down's syndrome.

The Bowels can be a focus for this remedy with problems like:
- ⊙ **IBS** – again affecting the smooth muscles within the gut.
- ⊙ **Colitis and spasmodic colon infection.**
- ⊙ **Rectal tenesmus**: The patient wants to pass stool, but cannot.

The **Bladder & Kidneys** have: **Incontinence**, worse in the evening. Nephritis.

DIABETES – has been cured with Pit. Gland, especially in the early stages of diagnosis.
- ⊙ The severity of the diabetes can also be determined by the Pituitary Gland.

EYES: Mydriasis: Pupils are much dilated.
- ⊙ Conjunctivitis and Blepharitis
- ⊙ Weeping: the patient cries involuntarily and even without noticing.

Head: Headaches, starting at the occiput and spreading towards the base, cervical column and shoulders.
- ⊙ Pulsating, throbbing headaches, related to hypertension.
- ⊙ Congestive headache < heat < at the end of the day.

HEART: – after an operation on the heart (by-pass operation, etc.) as it affects the smooth muscle tissue.
- ⊙ With any heart problem there is very often 'Nocturnal anguish', which is very much in the picture of this remedy.
- ⊙ Anxiety aggravated by nightfall. The patient 'feels his heart'.
- ⊙ **Hypertension** – also see Thyroid Gland – Angina Pectoris. Tachycardia.

Skin: Vitiligo. (The other two remedies listed are: Sep. & Thuja.)
- ⊙ Skin swollen – oedematous, itching, or eruptions of an urticaria type.

The PINEAL GLAND

THE THIRD EYE – also sometimes called the 'Spirit of love'
Influences the emotions, but also subject to atmospheric influences.

It was not that long ago that the function of the Pineal gland was not altogether clear (in fact, I still have some older books that state as much), and mystics just referred to it as the 'Third Eye'. Now we know that it produces two hormones, **Melatonin and Serotonin**, that control our circadian rhythms, operating strictly on a day and night cycle. Melatonin production <u>stops when it gets light</u> and <u>starts again at night-time</u>. It has proven to induce '**alpha**' <u>wave activity in the brain</u>, which is a more '**relaxed**' state to be in, and thus helps the body to 'heal'. Consequently is not only the 'Third Eye' but a 'peace gland', giving us 'inner peace' (one reason for meditation and visualisation of colours helping to increase the vibration of the auric field, as well as within). One can conclude that the pineal gland plays an active role in our health, not just on the physical level but on the mental level too.

While the baby is still in the uterus the pineal gland and the eyes consist of the same tissue, therefore a very good reason for it to be called our 'third eye'. Like the pupils of our eyes it adjusts constantly to the light available at the time, producing the aforementioned hormones and playing this vital part in our biorhythms.

Since we are very interested in what is going on in our 'second brain', the gut, it is interesting to note here that **Serotonin** is not just found in the pineal gland but also in high concentration in the intestinal mucosa. It stimulates the smooth (involuntary) muscles of the intestinal wall, and therefore a lack of this hormone could also be responsible for constipation (lack of transport of the chyme) and cuts down the acid secretion of the stomach.

The pineal gland is almost impossible to repertorise (except for seasonal affective disorder; SAD), whereas the pituitary and thyroid glands are to be found repeatedly in the repertory. Pineal gland in potency can be beneficial for the following:

- ⊚ In general it can help with the **calcium balance**, as well as **muscular dystrophy**.
- ⊚ In babies as a **consequence when the fontanelle will not close**.
- ⊚ In **MEN to prevent premature aging**, when hair begins to fall out (works closely with 'Thymus Gland' here).
- ⊚ **IN BOYS to curb premature adolescence before age 9** (this could also result from a tumour on the brain and therefore needs to be medically checked out and eliminated).
- ⊚ **In children to stem precocity**.

Seasonal affective disorder **(SAD)** is a problem that affects certain people (particularly in the northern hemisphere) in the winter months, when daylight hours are short and often without direct sunlight. The exact aetiology for SAD is not known, but one likely theory causing this depression is a lack of serotonin release in the body (triggered by exposure of the skin to sunlight) and this condition is now often treated with 'full spectrum light therapy'.

Earlier we learned about 'bio-photons' from the research of Prof. Popp in Germany and how important 'light in the body' is. A patient with SAD affected by the dark days will say that 'January and February are their worst months'! I have found that 'Pineal Gland' in potency 30c, weekly, is very helpful in those cases where winter has previously meant 'doom and gloom' to the patient. This remedy must surely be better than giving 'Prozac', which is a selective serotonin re-uptake inhibitor. It was praised as the 'happy pill' in cases of depression, but with side-effects of insomnia, headaches, nausea and restlessness I would not call it that at all.

The THYROID GLAND

'The Spirit of Life'
The Thyroid Gland is the 'glandular' link between the brain
and the reproductive organs.

The thyroid is responsible for the metabolic rate that affects the nervous system. It directly influences the circulation/respiration/tissue growth and repair. The two lobes of the thyroid gland lie in the neck, just behind the 'Adam's apple' on either side of the trachea, and unless there is a problem with enlargement (called 'goitre') it is not visible or palpable. The gland is slightly larger in women than in men.

Thyroxin, which **contains Iodine, is the best known hormone made by the thyroid** and **either an over or under production of this hormone leads to problems. The other two HORMONES are: Tri-iodothyronine,** which acts directly on almost all cells in the body, controlling the metabolic rate, and **Calcitonin**. Special cells in the thyroid produce Calcitonin and also constantly monitor the calcium balance in the blood, acting on the bones and interfering with the release of calcium when necessary. This kind of negative feedback mechanism is very common in the body.

As a remedy it was introduced as early as 1892 by the homœopath Murray, who called it THYROIDINUM and was later proved by a few other homœopaths by the names of Panos, Roger and Stephenson in 1963/64, as well as by Ghose. Miasmatically this is a 'mixed miasmatic remedy', with a strong tendency to the Tubercular miasm, like being '**irritable at the least opposition**', impatient, hysterical and of course having a '**tendency to allergies**'.

In his book 'Chemistry of Men' Dr Bernard Jensen called **Iodine** the '**metaboliser**', and if iodine is missing numerous problems arise; these include problems with infertility and impotence, mongolism and hyperactive children, lack of emotional control, elevated fears and on the other hand lethargy and depression. This metabolising gland regulates the pulse rate, helps to neutralise toxins in the body and calms the nerves. From clinical feedback we have: **Goitre**, **obesity** and **urine increased** as symptoms needing THYRIODINUM.

In the condition called '**Hyperthyroidism**' the person is:
- ⊙ very nervous and easily excitable, cannot sleep.
- ⊙ experiences weight loss despite a good appetite.
- ⊙ can suffer palpitations and sweating due to increased heat production!

In contrast in '**Hypothyroidism**' the opposite is true:
- ⊙ people with great sensitivity to cold.
- ⊙ sluggish, both mentally and physically.
- ⊙ want to sleep more.
- ⊙ put on weight.
- ⊙ skin is dry, possibly with puffiness of hands and face.
- ⊙ in females menstrual problems are typical: Menses **scanty – or too much/ too often – flooding etc**.

For over or under function of the thyroid, instead of taking Thyroxin give 'Thyroid Gland' in potency; a 30c every day for one month, followed by a 200c once a month. This helps to bring about balance and can avoid an operation. When repertorising look out for THYROID; you will by surprised how often you will find it listed.

Thyroid function lessens naturally after the age of 45. This is when all sorts of problems arise and very likely patients suddenly need high blood pressure pills even though they may have had low blood pressure all their life!
- ⊙ Consequently, consider Thyroid Gland for **High Blood pressure**.
- ⊙ The same goes for **PRE-ECLAMPSIA** in pregnancy as it will help to bring the blood pressure down. Like 'Pituitary Gland' in potency consider it in cases of **tendency to miscarriage**, giving Thyroid to help regulate the hormones.
- ⊙ Premature **LABOUR** can equally be stopped with Thyroid Gland.
- ⊙ For coming off HRT or after **Hysterectomy** give 'Thyroid Gland' for the first week, whole 'Ovary' for the second week, followed by 'Pineal' or 'Pituitary Gland' for the third week.

For men at about the same age when women enter the menopause, or later of course, thyroid in potency is listed when a 'benign enlargement' of the prostate is often a problem.

When it comes to **children** and their development the thyroid gland plays a huge role, with rubrics like:

- ⊚ **'Cretinism'** and **'Development delayed'** include Thyroid.
- ⊚ Part of this 'delay' could of course be due to **'Emaciation from nutritional imbalance'**. Correct food plays a huge role in a child's life. However, it might not be due to junk food but rather the thyroid gland delaying the natural development.
- ⊚ For example **'bedwetting'** can point to a thyroid problem. If this goes on for too long then think about giving this remedy daily in a low potency for a month, and then review.

Some babies having difficulty in **feeding, sleeping and suffering from constipation,** they could be born with underactivity of the thyroid. Usually babies are given a blood test and therefore any under-function should be detected promptly.

Another rubric in the children's section is:

- ⊚ **Hair growing on the face of children**. (In relation to the face, facial diagnosis is also useful; if the eyebrows are half missing it points to an imbalance in the thyroid.)
- ⊚ Also found in the children's section is **convulsion** (not to be confused with febrile fits) during **dentition** and **epilepsy**, especially in little boys.
- ⊚ **Psoriasis** of the skin can have its origin in a thyroid problem.
- ⊚ Similarly, Rosacea of the skin points to an under-function of this organ.
- ⊚ Thyroid Gland can help for all kinds of **ALLERGIES**, including those related to the Nosodes of Tub./Med./Psor.

After a **THYROIDECTOMY** give Thyroid Gland 30c, followed by **Ignatia 10M** (for the lump in the throat). Also after the removal of the thyroid gland, and for people having problems losing weight, it should be considered in potency to feed the etheric gland.

The thyroid gland being called the **'Vanity gland'**, gives clues when the body might be 'out of shape', which might not be pleasing to the eye, (nonetheless, beauty is always in the eye of the beholder).

OBESITY can be a real problem here, especially if thyroid problems are due to a family history. This can show itself at a very young age, with an <u>overweight young boy having problems with his testes</u>: **Undescended testicles!** With this problem it is very important for the homœopath to ask the mother about the pregnancy: Were there problems like **nausea and vomiting** (especially if this was going on for months), <u>oedema of the legs, hypertension, palpitation, dyspnoea, vertigo in pregnancy, and a possible history of miscarriages in the third months</u>? (All these give vital clues to an imbalance in the thyroid).

A teenager needing thyroid in potency **will quarrel with the family, yet is 'indifferent to everything'**. For those who have no plans for the future 'Thyroid' can give an impetus to become more creative, as this is the gland that helps to form habits and fosters creation. These habits can of course be positive as well as negative ones, therefore it is vital that we help children to maintain a mental balance, form objective thoughts and learn to express themselves, rather than allowing them to suffer from the 'delusion of being persecuted', with suspicion and mania developing. Before going on to the next remedy **Parathyroid,** I would like to mention **Thyroidinum.** Thyroidinum, (a combination of iodine and thyroid extract) is another remedy we can consider to balance the vital function of the thyroid.

In later years there can be problems with **'brittle bones'** or **'slow repair of broken bones'**, yet I feel here we should rather look at the next remedy as a prevention: The '**Parathyroid'**.

The PARATHYROID

The Parathyroid, as the name suggests, is part of the thyroid. These four pea-sized glands are located at the back of the Thyroid and produce a hormone that regulates the calcium and phosphor metabolism. If for any reason this is deficient then '**Hypoparathyroidism'**, tetany, or seizures may result. On the other hand if there is an imbalance from over-activity or '**Hyperparathyroidism'** then erosion of the bones and calculi (stones) in the urinary tract may occur. (Therefore, if the patient suffers from kidney or bladder-stones consider Parathyroid as a Sarcode.)

This overproduction of the parathyroid will increase the calcium in the blood by drawing it from the bones, leaving them 'brittle'. This imbalance could come as a result of a Thyroidectomy when the negative feedback discussed earlier (see section on Thyroid Gland) is missing after this vital organ has been removed; a tumour on the gland itself can have the same effect.

Parathyroid is **not** a remedy that you will find very often in the repertory. Whenever I do, however, I make a note of it: I once found it in the 'Disease chapter' under BESNIER-BOAK-SCHAUMANN morbus, also known as Besnier's prurigo, which are itchy eruptions of papules behind the knees and inside the elbows (part of Neurodermatitis atopica). There is information on this remedy, however, in Murphy's Lotus of clinical experience:

- ⊙ **Arthritis** (wrist, ankles, knees and hips, deformity of fingers).
- ⊙ **Bone disorders** and **Calcium deposits** (Fibrocystic osteitis).
- ⊙ **Kidney stones**.

Additionally it can be found under haematuria and polyuria, muscular hypotonia and multiple myeloma, osteoporosis, Paget's disease, and **Pancreatitis** (especially when chronic; worth taking note of as this would not naturally come to mind when thinking of this remedy). Furthermore we have:

- ⊙ **Uterine fibromyoma** (benign tumour in the muscle fibres of the uterus).
- ⊙ Controlling the **Calcium metabolism,** as mentioned, can work wonders in osteoporosis: 30c = 1 x weekly. (Too much Cortisone can have induced the osteoporosis.)
- ⊙ All sorts of **rheumatism**; bone pains.
- ⊙ **osteomalacia**; softening of bones (Psor. + Syph.).

This remedy is also suitable for '**growing pains'** in young children, usually between the ages of six and twelve, often with vague aches and pains in the limbs and affecting the calves, normally being worse at night. Considering that the calcium metabolism is not in balance, a 'split dose' 30c will give a boost to the Parathyroid. In potency this will have a positive impact on the child's sleep, as well as on the **'restless legs'** that are associated with the thyroid, since copper is the metal of the Throat chakra and this needs to work together with zinc to be in 'harmony' within the body.

For this remedy in relation to teeth we have:

- ⊙ **Teething problems in children**, which I would support with Calc-p. or Calc-fl., as well as Calc-carb. as Tissue Salts, too.
- ⊙ 'Crumbling' teeth would be a problem where Parathyroid can help.
- ⊙ Black roots, or losing teeth in pregnancy.

Other conditions that may be helped by Parathyroid are: **Chilblains and Varicose Veins; Parkinson's** disease (even if not cured, can stop progression).

Lastly, I would like to mention problems with food:

- **Anorexia;**
- Gastric acidity, painful after meals with gastric attacks;
- sickness in pregnancy;
- stomach and duodenal ulcers (worst case – vomiting blood);
- not forgetting the **Mind**, where we can have mental confusion, depression and agitation.

The THYMUS GLAND

The Gland for 'PURIFICATION AND IMMUNITY'

If removed the '**personality**' changes and the immune system is totally impaired.

The Thymus Gland has two lobes and lies in the upper part of the chest, in front of the trachea (windpipe) and is part of the Heart Chakra. It is interesting to note that the name 'Thymus' was created by Galen in the second century AD, as the gland resembled a bunch of thyme flowers. Galen even declared it as the 'seat of the soul', which then became a subject of much speculation. However, it was not until 1960 that the function of the thymus was finally known. Thanks to modern medicine we now know that the two lobes are divided into the outer cortex and the medulla, the inner portion. The cortex resembles lymphoid tissue and is made of masses of small cells called **thymocytes**. The medulla is of a more loosely connected tissue and contains fewer lymphocytes. These lymphocytes are also known as T-cells and take part in the body's defence against viruses and other infections. The second lymphocytes are B-lymphocytes ('B' for bursa or bone-marrow dependent), or white blood cells, which are produced in the bone marrow and are concerned with the production and circulation of humeral antibodies. The thymus gland plays its part in the response to any infection from the 12th week of gestation up to puberty, when it is known to shrink. In children, immunodeficiency disorders may arise as a result of abnormal development of the thymus.

Disorder: The thymus gland can be affected by tumours and the whole gland can in fact be removed. A patient of mine had to have his thymus gland removed for this very reason. He had a tumour and thus had this gland removed over 10 years ago. Medically speaking having this removed was no problem, nevertheless he has never been well since. By giving him 'Thymus Gland' as a remedy in a 30c once a week he felt for the first time that 'things are getting better' and was positive about his recovery. By feeding his etheric gland also other problems have subsided.

Other abnormal enlargement of the thymus may occur in several conditions, including:

- ⊙ **Myasthenia gravis,**
- ⊙ **acromegaly,**
- ⊙ **thyrotoxicosis** and **Addison's disease.**
- ⊙ **Myasthenia gravis** is also sometimes associated with **thymomas** (tumours of the thymus)

while in other patients with the same condition changes have taken place due to an inflammation of the gland called **thymitis**.

The remedy **Thymus Gland** had a meditative proving by the Guild of Homœopaths and these are some of my notes from a lecture in November 1998.

Thymus Gland for Children

- Resembles many other Polychrests, especially for children needing: **Sil., Calc-carb., Carc., Tub.**
- **Children have a lot of acute illnesses,** a compromised immune system, and look fragile.
- **Slowness in development: mentally,** dentition, walking, speech, growth etc.
- **Ill effects of vaccination**; especially on growth and nutrition.
- **NBWS childhood illness, especially measles and chickenpox.**
- **Worried looking babies**: worry around eyes and lines on forehead.
- **Extremes of behaviour**: Obsessive and over fastidious, upset out of all proportion.
- **Excessively affectionate children**: always telling mummy they love her.

Thymus Gland for Adults

- **Adults are often overweight and sluggish.**
- **Adults:** present deeper and darker picture: Trauma – emotional.
- **People who have never been mothered**; cannot find that love within themselves.
- History of trauma and abuse in childhood, especially sexual abuse; great fear of being hurt.
- **Serious road accidents; injury to the head and/or spinal cord.**
- **Identity crisis** (the thymus creates a sense of identity on the cellular level).
- **NBWS symptoms produced by acute or prolonged stress, also at stressful times or events.**
- **Food allergies** are an aspect of a generally impaired immune system.
- After acute illness or acute episodes of chronic illness, Thymus gland will speed up recovery.

Thymus Gland in potency can make a lot of difference and needs to be repeated, maybe once or twice a week. As a 3x or 6x potency it can be used as support on the physical/emotional/spiritual level to enhance the effect of the Polychrests. This remedy facilitates indicated remedies that are not doing enough. It works very well in low potency either on its own or in combination with other remedies, or as an intercurrent. It is useful to give as an intercurrent to men, middle age onwards, particularly where there are prostate problems (for women, give Thyroidinum).

For treatment after vaccination, even where there are no obvious presenting symptoms, give for example: SIT (Syph.+Ign.+Th.G.) or SAT (Syph.+Ars.Alb.+Th.G.), 12x, 15x or 30c weekly, with vaccine remedy 30c monthly.

This may be continued for 6 months alongside constitutional treatment. A reaction to the thymus combination in the form of getting a 'temperature' indicates that the immune system is starting to function better and the remedy needs to be given less often in a higher potency, using Belladonna for the temperature when the need arises. Thuja also works well for this and can be used alongside Thymus Gland.

The PANCREAS

The Gland of JOY – 'to trust in the future' and 'sweetness of life'.

The pancreas is located on the left side of the body, behind the stomach, and has two functions: One is to produce pancreatic juice, which contains digestive enzymes that pass into the duodenum (the first part of the small intestine) via the pancreatic duct; the other function is to produce the hormones **insulin, glucagon and somatostatin**, a polypeptide hormone secreted by the islets of Langerhans, which also monitor the concentration of glucose in the blood.

Glucose is the main fuel for the body and in the absence of insulin on the cell membranes, which act like 'gate keepers', glucose cannot get through and therefore accumulates in the blood. In this condition when the body requires more fuel it will call on the muscles to release more glucose, leading to 'wasting muscles' and diabetes.

Digestive enzymes are crucial for the correct breakdown of ingesting fat, protein and carbohydrates, while the imbalance in the production of insulin leads to complaints such as diabetes, as mentioned above. Our western diet is far too 'sweet', with lots of fizzy drinks for example; this overuse of sugar, either real or artificial sweeteners, can lead to an early onset of the disease.

From my own experience I have found that giving **Pancreas 30c** once a week for one month has improved the digestive system for a lot of my patients, as well as reducing the urgency to urinate too often, either in the day or at night. These were patients who were not classed as diabetics, but often I could see the pre-diabetic state from the iris. If not spotted in the iris, the symptoms of bloating after meals, feeling very tired, plus being thirsty often, was a good reason to give either **Pancreas 30c** as mentioned above, or start the patient on '**Pancreas Support**'. **Pancreas Support** is a combination of three remedies in low potency: **Pancreatinum, Iris and Phosphorus**. Taking Pancreas Support after each meal for at least a month brings an improvement; the patient feels more alert after meals and the uncomfortable feeling of everything being too tight around the waist automatically goes. Often they manage to lose a little weight too, as the 'sweet-craving' lessens considerably.

Pancreatitis, the inflammation of the pancreas, either acute or chronic (especially in alcoholism), can be helped with **Pancreas Support** three times daily to prevent recurring episodes of unpleasant symptoms. These symptoms include a sudden severe pain in the centre of the abdomen, often occurring within 12 hours after a heavy meal with alcohol. (Acute Pancreatitis can sometimes be mistaken for a heart attack, as the pains are high in the abdomen and spread through to the back.) Other benefits of this remedy include:

- ⊚ **Pancreas 30c once a month reduces the need to inject Insulin.**
- ⊚ For **polycystic ovaries** (or chocolate cysts) give Pancreas 30c + Bowel Nosode.

The other remedy to consider here is **PANCREATINUM:** This is a remedy that we do know a little about, as Burnett says it has often been of **great service in gout**.

The SPLEEN

Located next to the **PANCREAS** is the **SPLEEN**. Spleen in potency can be given for the effects of over-studying! The **pancreas and the spleen both belong to the Sacral Chakra**; in fact in German we call this Chakra the 'Milz' Chakra, after the spleen. As a remedy we know it as '**Splenum**' or Spleen.

The **Spleen** is an unpaired organ, situated on the left upper part of the abdomen between the stomach and the left kidney. It is pliable and purple in colour and only 125 mm in length. The spleen has several functions during our lifetime. In foetal life and the new born child it is the site of red blood cell formation and is part of the immune system. Later the bone marrow takes over this job and the spleen acts as a blood reservoir.

Although the spleen is not absolutely vital to the body and can be removed (for example after a car accident when there is severe internal bleeding resulting from a rupture of the spleen) it certainly has an important function as part of the immune system. Another reason for the removal of the spleen is the enlargement due to '**Anaemia**', such as inherited '**Spherocytosis**', '**Thalassaemia**' or '**Lymphomas**' of the spleen.

Glandular Fever often affects teenagers or young adults when going through examination times. We can see how spleen in potency could help them to get over this otherwise very tiring disease that usually takes months to recovery from. This would speed up the process to be in good form again. The **Cytomegalovirus** in potency is to be considered in cases of **NBWS glandular fever**. During infections such as **Malaria, Typhoid fever and TB** it is also a good idea to **support the Spleen**, as they will also cause enlargement of the organ.

SECRETIN

Secretin is not an organ, rather a hormone secreted by the mucous membrane of the duodenum, the first part of the small intestine. The remedy Secretin encourages the production of pancreatic juice and has been found to be very helpful in some cases of Autism (although not every autistic child will respond favourably to this remedy). Personally I have not noticed any change in autistic children who I have treated with Secretin, yet this does not mean that some children will not benefit from it.

The benefit of Secretin was highlighted by one mother in America after her son was successfully treated with it. She then made it public that this could be of use in others who have an overgrowth of yeast in the gut. This overgrowth of yeast makes the children 'allergic' to all sorts of foods, which can make them hyperactive as the food itself causes a toxin stimulating the brain in a negative way.

Therapeutically Secretin can be useful for **constipation and indigestion** as it stimulates the pancreatic secretion to increase peristalsis of the intestines, thus reducing fermentation and putrefaction. It is usually used in low potency of either 3x or 6x several times daily.

'**Earthdragon**' was an old fashioned remedy for the gut problems in Asian medicine. Now we have **Earthworm**, or **Lumbricus Terr.**, which can be very helpful if the gut problems go back to vaccination damage. It helps to repair damaged tissue on a cellular level and has an affinity with the Bowel Nosodes **Morgan Pure** and **Morgan Gaertner**. **Earthworm** can assist **Okoubaka** in wheat allergy.

The KIDNEYS

The Kidneys are a pair of bean-shaped structures, each 11cm long and situated close to the spine in the upper part of the abdomen. They are the principle organs of excretion of the water soluble waste products and regulate the fluids in the body of sodium, potassium and hydrogen content and their associated anions. It is estimated that in 24 hours the kidneys filter between 150 and 200 litres of blood/plasma; if renal failure should occur a dialysis machine can perform this task. Such failure can either be acute or chronic when a transplant might be needed. The acute form may occur due to a 'crush' accident, or an incompatible blood transfusion (which should never happen in reality). It may also arise from <u>mercury poisoning</u> (we should not forget the negative effects on the body from toxic vapours inhaled when having several amalgam fillings removed at once), or from too many vaccinations, for example before a trip around the World. (I only mention this here as the daughter of a friend of mine had all the vaccines 'necessary for a trip around the World' within a very short period of time, before leaving on a 'gap-year' of her studies. Within two weeks of leaving England, however, she was so ill that she had to give up her trip and come home!) Haemorrhages in the later stages of pregnancy could also be a sign of kidney failure.

When the kidneys fail to act, the solids of the waste products accumulate in the blood, resulting in a poisoning of the body, also known as **Uraemia.** In general when the blood-vessels in the kidney are diseased and partially closed by arteriosclerosis, the blood pressure rises.

Kidney in potency can help in any case of Kidney disease! (Related to Lyc., Berb., Hydr.)

Renal Carbuncles, which at one time was commonly caused due to the well known **Staphylococcus aureus**. These days Staphylococcus is very much in the news as a 'hospital-acquired' infection. We know that this gram-positive bacterium is widely distributed in the environment and is often present on the skin and in the nasal passages in a healthy person. Pus formation is the feature in those whose immune system is compromised, which can result in <u>carbuncles, boils, impetigo</u> and other <u>skin problems</u>, but can also cause more serious deep infections, leading to <u>septicaemia, osteomyelitis,</u> <u>enteritis</u> or <u>pneumonia</u>. Certain strains of Staphylococcal may produce **food poisoning**. I have mentioned the Staphylococcus aureus infections here as the kidney will have to 'filter' the pus. Since kidneys are always linked to **Skin problems** we should consider giving both Kidney and Staphylococcus aureus in potency in acute scenarios of the diseases mentioned above.

For **kidney stones** give 'Calculus Renalis' (which is potentised kidney stone), since it can help to break down kidney stones and avoid those dreadfully painful colics when passing them, plus prevent them from forming again. <u>It will also help 'arthritic</u> <u>nodules' and removes or 'prevents tartar on teeth'.</u>

Kidney stones can be formed of different 'substances', too. For example, when 'uric acid' is abnormally high, as in patients suffering from gout, kidney stones may develop. Equally, when people use artificial sweeteners in excess the body does not seem to be able to eliminate it sufficiently and forms a new kind of stone, not seen before according to a recent report I read in Germany.

Above the kidneys we have the Adrenal Glands:

The ADRENAL GLANDS

READY FOR EMERGENCY – producing ADRENALIN

The Adrenal Glands are situated above the Kidneys – small 'yellowish triangles'.

These endocrine glands are the instruments that help to determine the entire electrical potentials of the human body. They are responsible for the sympathetic nerves and their secretions regulate the blood pressure and control the contraction of muscles and the heartbeat. The adrenal glands produce **50 different natural steroid hormones**, some of which are involved in the conversion of dietary protein and fat into glucose, while others suppress inflammation and promote healing. These glands also regulate the <u>iron content in the blood</u>, which is balanced in the kidneys. Adrenal exhaustion has become a 'modern disease' called **STRESS**, which is widespread with millions apparently 'suffering' from it. We could also call it 'burn-out', and looking at the **MIND** section we find words like: <u>Apathy, despondence and nervousness</u>, as well as a lack of interest in anything, no ambition, disinclination for mental work, and an absence of 'grit'! We also find **lack of concentration**, and tiredness (runs out of energy fast). Evenings are the time when it shows most that the adrenal glands are exhausted as the body clock for the adrenals is from 3 PM to 3 AM, while the thyroid time is from 3 AM to 3 PM. Exhaustion of the adrenal gland would show with 'sleepiness in the afternoon', even after a good night's sleep.

Adrenal failure may be due to a disorder called **'Addison's Disease'**, resulting in general weakness, anaemia and wasting away. The skin will also change colour, first turning yellow and then brown, or in other patients a low blood pressure may result. Usually the medical treatment is a hormone injection of 'Corticosteroid'. However, 'Adrenalin', which is the extract of the adrenal glands, is known to have cured a number of cases and arrested others.

From Clinical experience:
- **Adrenal neuralgias.**
- **Bronzed skin.**
- **Debility, Haematuria.**
- **Hyperaemia.**
- **Palpitations and Tachycardia.**

Food: Needs to eat all the time, and thirst of large quantities of water, increased in the evening. There can be nausea before a meal, yet appetite is good once beginning to eat. In the **Abdomen** there can be a lot of rumbling; Borborygmus, plus belching after a meal and sudden diarrhoea.

Adrenalin 30c can be given up to once a day for a prolonged period after a long term use of **Cortisone**. It will help to balance the adrenal glands and stimulate them into proper action, and supports the possibility to reduce the need for medication in the long run. Another remedy to consider here is **A.C.T.H. 30c**, which **can be used after a prolonged use of steroids to rebalance the adrenal glands.**

GONADS – Energy Centres of Life

The gonads are the sex glands and produce internal secretions that are distributed by the blood in order to stimulate and revitalise all the other glands and organs in the body, therefore also creating a certain amount of the external secretions. Let us therefore now consider the sex glands; ladies first:

The UTERUS

The uterus is an elongated muscular organ of only 8cm in length in the non-pregnant woman, weighing about 60-90 grams. This pear shaped organ increases its weight to about 1 kg at the end of a full-term pregnancy and thus keeping the muscles in good shape is vital for a successful pregnancy. Therefore, in the case of a prolapsed uterus from the previous pregnancy, before starting the next baby it is a good idea to tone the uterus with this remedy in potency 30c once a week for a few weeks. (Often a prolapse indicates potassium deficiency, thus Kali-Carb. may be used as well.)

- **Uterus 30c** for allopathic devastation of the female reproductive organ, such as after a **hysterectomy**, or a **Dilatation and Curettage (D&C)**.

PYROGEN, although not a Sarcode but a Nosode, can also be considered in uterine disorders through abortions, miscarriages or injuries (NBWS). Where we have an intense septic state we can give Pyrogen as well as the indicated remedy and **Uterus** in potency afterwards, to tone the organ again.

The OVARIES

The name OVARIES comes from the Greek word for 'testes' and the 2nd Century Greek physician Galen called them *Orchei*.

Orchid flowers were also named after testicles because the watery bulb at the base of the plant looks like a wrinkled scrotum. A fourth Century bishop is supposed to have commented that 'women had the same equipment as him, except that theirs was inside the body and not outside'. Well, I guess he had a point, to an extent. These two almond shaped glands are 3cm long and 2cm wide. They secrete and respond to hormones and are responsible for ovulation once a month. Throughout the female reproductive cycle a single ovum should be released on about day 15, sometimes accompanied by what is called the 'Mittelschmerz' (in German literally meaning 'middle-pain'). When the ovaries cease to function a woman enters the menopause.

Oophorinum is the ovarian extract that we can use as a remedy for the following problems with the ovaries:

- **Surgical removal of the ovaries**.
- **SKIN:** Since the ovaries are responsible for the 'female' characteristics in women, such as a high-pitched voice, they are also of importance when it comes to beautiful skin and under 'Acne Rosacea' we find 'Ovary Gland' or 'Oophorinum' listed.
- **Oophorinum** has been found useful in a 30x potency to remove unwanted facial hair in women (given 3 times daily for a few months).
- For **Infertility, Oophorinum** would be on obvious choice, yet **Folliculinum** is the other well-known one, as well as **Corpus Luteum**.
- **Folliculinum: a tonic for the ovaries, especially after hormonal abuse.** (The pill or coming off HRT.)

The CORPUS LUTEUM

Corpus Luteum means the '**Yellow Body**', which is vital for fertility. The luteinising hormone from the pituitary gland splits the follicles open, sometimes causing a little 'spotting' mid-cycle, and releases the ovum down the fallopian tubes. This surge of hormones can be detected by an ovulation predictor kit, for those who plan a pregnancy.

If pregnancy occurs then the corpus luteum lives on and is essential for the survival of the foetus, especially the first 42 days, after which the placenta should take over.

In the absence of pregnancy, however, the corpus luteum regresses 10 days after ovulation and becomes the **corpus albicans**, the **'white body'**. Thus we can see why this remedy can be used successfully for the following problems:

- **Infertility without cause (potency 30c weekly when women do not ovulate);**
- **Sickness in pregnancy that goes on and on** (also consider thyroid gland);
- **pre-menstrual syndrome (PMS)**, when very emotional.

The PLACENTA

The placenta develops from foetal tissue and is the physical link from mother to baby during pregnancy. When expelled at the time of birth shortly after the baby it weighs about 600g. It is disc-shaped, 2cm thick and about 16cm in diameter.

The hormones **Oestrogen and Progesterone**, as well as chorionic gonadotrophin (HCG), are produced by the placenta, the latter being found in high levels in the urine when pregnant, which forms the basis of a pregnancy test. Later on these hormones prepare the breast for lactation.

The **Placenta** in potency can help in the following cases:

- **Placenta** and the **Pituitary Gland** work very much together, thus both can help to address **nausea/vomiting in pregnancy**, and **pre-eclampsia**.
- When the baby is not thriving, in spite of loving care. **For breastfed babies who do not thrive; mother's milk is not enough, or not much good.**
- **Post natal depression or for any kind of over-drugging at birth.**
- Patients who have had a stillborn child to avoid the same scenario next time.
- **A tendency to miscarry and for ill effects of repeated miscarriages (NBWS).** Give as soon as the patient is pregnant = 200c.

Related to Urtica-u., Alfalfa, Phytolacca, Lac-h., as well as to Baryta-c., Thyroid Gland and Pit. Gland.

The MAMMARY GLANDS

These two glands, together with connective and adipose tissue, form the breasts and are needed for lactation to feed the infant. In potency any problems with breastfeeding could be addressed with this remedy. It has also been helpful in profuse menstruation, or too frequent menstruations in young girls. **Uterine fibroids** can call for this remedy.

The PROSTATE GLAND

The prostate gland in size is about the dimensions of a chestnut and is situated in the rectum, immediately under the bladder. At birth it weighs just a few grams, enlarging to full size during puberty under the **androgen** hormone. Further enlargement is rare before the age of 30, unless through a sexually transmitted disease, yet men over 50 often have a benign enlargement usually interfering with urination, as the enlarged prostate compresses the urethra. Thus '**Prostate Gland**' in potency can be used for any problems of **incontinence in old men,** and for **enlarged** or **benign tumours**. (There is no reason why it cannot be given in cancerous cases, either.)

I have recently given it very successfully to an elderly man who complained about problems with urination, as well as occasional pains in the lower abdomen and lower back and around the rectum. Not something men like to talk about at all, but in this case while waiting for a hospital consultant to have a look (in a couple of months' time) I suggested that some remedies may help. As I had very successfully treated another elderly man (aged 90) for cancer of the prostate the previous year the objective was that there was 'no harm in trying!' After being on Prostate 30c twice a week within two weeks the pain was the first to subside. The medical doctor had told him that there was nothing to worry about in the first place! Well, that might be so, but the gentleman in question is 80 years old and very frightened of what might be found. Therefore I also gave him Ars. Alb. 200c, which took the fear away.

Relates to: THUJA, Hydr., Rhodo., Clem.

Other remedies to consider: CON., DAM., DIG., PULS., SEL., STAPH.,

Sabal serrulata, also known as Saw Palmetto, give several times daily in low potency daily as support.

The TESTES and ORCHITINUM

Testicles or Testes are the male reproductive organs or gonads. These two glands descend before birth into the lower part of the abdomen into a fold pouch known as the scrotum. Apart from producing the main male sex hormone **testosterone**, which is responsible for the development of male characteristics, they also produce spermatozoa. Testicular extract as a Sarcode is the remedy **ORCHITINUM**. Given as a remedy it can have the following benefits:

- ⊙ Clinically it has been used successfully for the **menopause, male as well as female.**
- ⊙ The practitioner formerly used it in cases of **sexual weakness**, and **premature senility**.
- ⊙ It can be given to woman with fertility problems, while 'Whole Ovary' can be given to the man; each remedy balances the masculine/feminine 'energy' in the sexual sphere.
- ⊙ **Low energy in men; impotence**. Give once a week = 30c for reproductive problems.
- ⊙ Un-descended testes in little boys; in fact any problems with the testicles.
- ⊙ **In Men: high blood pressure** in the typical **Nux-vom.** and **Lycopodium type.**
- ⊙ It is also complementary to 'Pituitrin' (Pituitary extract).

Chapter SEVEN

Introduction to the CELL or TISSUE SALTS

In Germany 'Biochemie' was the label originally given to the cell (or tissue) salts. The words BIO, for life, and CHEMIE, for the study of substances, elements and compounds and their relation to each other, give us a clue to the essence of 'biochemistry'. The idea of healing the body with tissue salts was introduced in the 19th Century when the scientific field of chemistry was still in its infancy. At this time just 12 of these tissue salts were used and are still sufficient to balance the body. They are prepared in much the same way as homœopathic remedies, in a potency of 6x. I have included an introduction to the tissue salts here since I always suggest that the 'Bowel Nosode Programme' should be supported by giving these salts, and therefore it is important to have a better understanding of them.

The first person to make this therapy popular was **Dr Wilhelm Heinrich Schuessler, M.D.,** born on 21st August 1821 near Oldenburg in northern Germany. The popularity of these tissue salts did not wane after his death and remained a very easy household 'first aid tool'. Since there are only 12 types to choose from they were easy to prescribe and my mother would often resort first to these tissue salts for cases of minor ills and see if we got better, before consulting the doctor.

At the time of Schuessler's birth Hahnemann was 66 years old and although I am sure that the two never met, Schuessler certainly studied Homœopathy as a young doctor. Schuessler died of a stroke on 30th March 1989 age 77. He was a contemporary of Prof. Rudolf Virchow, who was born in Pommern in Germany in 1821 and was one of the foremost scientists of his day. Virchow discovered that the human body is composed of an enormous number of tiny, living cells, each made up of an infinitesimal but perfectly balanced quantity of three types of materials, coining the statement that *'the disease of the body is equal to the disease of the cell'*. This understanding of how the cells work was fundamental to Dr Schuessler and his **'CELL-SALT-THERAPY'**, the **TISSUE Salts**.

Another scientist living in Germany at this time was Prof. Jakob Moleschott, born in 1822 in Herzogenbusch, Germany. In his book 'Der Kreislauf des Lebens' (The Wheel of Life) he wrote that 'disease commences after the loss of the inorganic salts'. While in Homœopathy we say **'Similia similibus curentur'**, in biochemistry we have **'that what is lacking needs to be supplemented'** (from the German 'Fehlendes werde durch Fehlendes ersetzt').

The tissue salts are **not** drugs in any sense of the word, as they are potentised inorganic elements. They simply provide a 'stimulant' to speed up better assimilation and thus bring back balance and harmony to the system, which spells **'health and happiness'**. Let me recount a little bit of the life of Heinrich Schuessler and how he 'discovered' them for his own practise.

Young Heinrich's father worked for the government in a very poorly paid job at the time and did not earn enough money to send his very talented son to school. Thus he studied at home from books and learned Latin, Greek, French, English, Spanish and Italian. Later he even studied Sanskrit! (I believe that he may have 're-discovered' the tissue salt therapy while studying this ancient language, as most people are not aware that this is more than just a language, it is an ancient science.)

While he was growing up in Germany Homœopathy became very popular. In fact, it was so much in demand that he decided to become a lay-prescriber himself, as he was so keen to help people with their health problems. His brother, realising his passion for medicine, helped to fund his college/university fees. He studied extremely hard and qualified as a medical doctor in only 5 semesters (2.5 years) at the University of Giessen. In 1857, after internships in Berlin, Paris and Prague, he started practising classical Homœopathy and was one of the first doctors to do so in his home town of Oldenburg. For 15 years he strictly defended any attacks from fellow doctors against this wonderful 'Art of Healing'. The only criticism he had about Homœopathy was the already large and ever increasing number of remedies. He felt that you had to be a great master to use 'all these remedies' successfully, like playing a 'super-organ' with lots of registers to 'push in and pull out'. On this theme he is supposed to have commented: 'that Mozart composed his beautiful music on a very small 'spinet' (mini-organ), and yet it is very peaceful and lovely to listen to'. Well, he would be astonished, or should I say horrified, to find that the list of remedies is forever growing with over 3000 now, while in Hahnemann's day I believe it was fewer than 100.

During his time as a Homœopath Dr Schuessler started to study the 'Mineral Salts' of the body, especially those he found in the ashes of cremated bodies, where he repeatedly found the same twelve salts. He noted that when these were potentised in the homœopathic way a very profound and deep acting remedy to treat deficiency resulted! There is nothing miraculous in the action of these remedies and yet the more recent discoveries in the field of the biological research and the finding of the present day biochemists confirm its teaching. In fact later discoveries made after his death serve and pay handsome tribute to the wonderful insight and true medical genius of Dr Schuessler, the founder of the 'Biochemistry' of the body.

One of the most striking features when it comes to select a remedy is that it requires only twelve remedies to learn and to choose from. A shortage or deficiency of one or several of these vital mineral substances may arise from a variety of causes: **injuries, self-poisoning, environmental toxins, STRESS, etc.** Obviously if the cells do not receive their proper nourishment or are not cleansed of the poisonous waste material resulting from cellular activity, ill-health becomes inevitable. The inorganic (mineral) elements, although present in much smaller quantities, are really vital elements, active 'workers', if you like, which utilise the organic substances in building the millions of cells of which the body is composed. To start with Dr Schuessler worked with 11 mineral salts numbering them from 1 to 11 (Calc-fl. No. 12 was added later). After 1872 Dr Schuessler treated patients exclusively in his 'new' way, calling the method 'BIOCHEMIE' and in 1874 for the first time he published the findings he had made and the way he treated his patients. Until his death in 1898 this was republished 25 times, proving its great success.

It is interesting to note that the word SALT is actually an old word for **Earth!** When talking about SALT we automatically think of cooking salt or of the sea and SALT-WATER, forgetting that **60%** of the human body is liquid (water; 45% intracellular body-fluids and 15% extra-cellular body-fluids). As we all started life from the sea we need to 'supply' our bodies with salt as we DO NOT make it within. If we do not get the essential salts we get sick: They are the **'Guardians of our health'**.

These mineral or tissue salts can be divided into **positive and negative IONS** (cations and anions, respectively) in the body, and this is how they act in the body (<u>not</u> common knowledge in Schuessler's time):

- ◉ Positively loaded are the **POTASSIUM/CALCIUM/SODIUM** and **MAGNESIUM.**
- ◉ Negatively loaded are the **CHLORIDES/PHOSPHATES and SULPHATES.**

- **POTASSIUM** is the most important positively charged intercellular fluid, acting as a catalyst for oxygen in the metabolism. The cells have 60 times more potassium than the surrounding fluids.
- **SODIUM** is the most positively loaded mineral in the extra-cellular fluid and thus does the opposite, helping to keep the acid/alkaline (pH) balance.
- **CALCIUM**, like Natrum, helps to keep the acid/alkaline balance but it is not found so much in the fluids, with 75% being located in the bones. While Potassium acts as a stimulator, calcium helps to 'calm' things. The rhythm of the heart beat depends very much on calcium. Calcium is very much needed in the blood, as without it could not clot.
- **MAGNESIUM** is also positively charged and is the opposite of Calcium, thus is an antagonist, yet will help to calm nerves. Similar to calcium it will help to normalise everything.
- The negative **Chloride** ions are hardly found within the cells but help to stabilise the extra-cellular pressure (OSMOSIS).
- The negative **Phosphor** ions help to regulate the sugar metabolism and increase nerve activity.
- The negative **Sulphates** are suitable for the 'detoxification' of the body, especially the liver.

Cleansing the system could be started, for example, with **three** tissue salts:

1. **Calc-s.** – helps to purify the **blood.**
2. **Kali-m.** – correct **sluggishness** and **repair** any damage.
3. **Nat-s.** – detoxify the **liver.**

Correction of past errors: If the patient does not respond well due to too many drugs taken in the past, two tissue salts can be given in alteration:

Nat-m. plus **Kali-s.** = 3 doses of each remedy taken daily for 2-3 weeks (adults 4 pills, children 2, and babies 1).

In long standing illnesses the response can be slow and these little tablets need to be taken at regular intervals, as often as 4 to 6 times daily for six months or more. In acute cases they can be repeated every 15-30 minutes until the symptoms subside.

In order to understand the tissue salts and the reasons for giving them as support with the Bowel Nosodes Programme I would like to introduce another supporter of BIOCHEMISTRY:

Dr George Washington Carey was born on 7th September 1845 in Dixon, Illinois to a large family. When he was one and a half his family left Illinois by wagon in true pioneering spirit and moved to Oregon, a journey which took them about 6 months. Here again we have a bright child that had no formal education, yet the parents provided what they could. In fact he was a very delicate child and his parents never thought that he would grow to manhood. He spent his early years on the farm and being a talented musician provided music in the evenings for entertainment. He even became the leader of the village orchestra. In his early forties he became a postmaster, yet when hearing about the science of biochemistry he resigned from this job to devote his life to its studies. Carey also had a great interest in ASTROLOGY and attributed one tissue salt to each sign of the ZODIAC, thus he gave us a unique way of looking at the biochemistry from another angle.

Especially now that we have entered the AQUARIAN age, also called the age of the 'Son of Man', we must change our vibration; we are forced to do so in order to move up into the next dimension. The mind must begin to expand and the animal-man at last must make a decided effort to purify himself of his animal nature and become really humane: Animal desires are below the Solar Plexus. In the NEW AGE we have to learn to think with the heart and love with the brain: We need to 'lift-off' to be lifted up to the 'third eye'.

In the bible we have the expression **'know the truth and the truth shall set you free'**, free from sickness, from sorrow or from fear of death, for death truly is the last enemy to overcome in some people's mind. Apart from accidents, death resulting from dis-ease is 'starvation of the cells' and a disharmony in the chemical elements. This is one of the very reasons why we should not poison ourselves with alcohol or tobacco, for example, which Dr Carey realised and gave up in his forties, never to touch them again. He recognised the effect that these toxins had on the delicate tissue, the membranes and the glands, which the Scriptures call **'the Temple of GOD'**!

Dr Carey worked tirelessly to spread the message, lecturing in his later life on his findings in places as far away as Australia. He wrote several books on this subject so dear to his heart: *The tree of Life* and the *God-man, the Word Made Flesh*, plus *The Chemistry of Life* and *The Chemistry and Wonders of the Human Body.* Carey passed away on 17th November 1924 after a lecture he gave in San Diego.

Dr Carey composed a poem on BIOCHEMISTRY, which expresses the essence of the tissue salts and I would like to share it with the reader, here:

> Acid and Alkali acting,
> Process and acting again,
> Operation, transmuting, fomenting,
> In throes and spasms of pain.
> Uniting, reaching, creating,
> Like souls 'passing under the rod',
> Some people call it Chemistry,
> And others call it God.

TISSUE SALTS & BACH FLOWER ESSENCES
According to Star Sign

Star Sign	Element	Planet	Date	Tissue Salt	Bach Flower Essence
ARIES The lamb of God	Cardinal – Fire	Mars	21.03-20.04	Kali-p. 'vehicle of consciousness'	Impatient
TAURUS The winged bull	Fixed – Earth	Venus	21.04-21.05	Nat-s. The cleanser	Gentian
GEMINI The twins	Mutable – Air	Mercury	22.05-21.06	Kali-m. The 'spinning salt'	Cerato
CANCER The crab (the mother sign)	Cardinal – Water	Moon	22.06-23.07	Calc-f. The 'natural flax'	Clematis
LEO – the Lion The heart of the Zodiac	Fixed Fire	Sun	24.07-23.08	Mag-p. The 'moving salt'	Vervain
VIRGO The Virgin Mary	Mutable – Earth	Mercury	24.08-23.09	Kali-s. (Puls.) The 'oil' – the 'lubricator'	Centaury
LIBRA The scale or balance	Cardinal – Air	Venus	24.09-23.10	Nat-p. The 'neutralizer' or 'balancing salt'	Scleranthus
SCORPIO The sting in the tail	Fixed – Water	Pluto / Mars	24.10-22.11	Calc-s. 'gypsum' or 'plaster of Paris'	Chicory
SAGITTARIUS The archer, aiming high	Mutable – Fire	Jupiter	23.11-21.12	Silicea pure flint	Agrimony
CAPRICORN The goat	Cardinal – Earth	Saturn	22.12-20.01	Calc-p. 'living limestone'	Mimulus
AQUARIUS The water bearer	Fixed – Air	Uranus / Saturn	21.01-21.02	Nat-m. saline fluid – our 'inner sea'	Water Violet
PISCES The fish that swims in the pure SEA	Mutable Water	Neptune / Jupiter	22.02-20.03	Ferr-p. 'fountain of life'	Rock Rose

Some may want to consider the remedies in terms of polarities, which are as follows:

Aries – Libra

Taurus – Scorpio

Gemini – Sagittarius

Cancer – Capricorn

Leo – Aquarius

Virgo – Pisces

The Main Focus of Physical Problems: Choosing Cell Salts

- **Calc. Fluor. – for vascular system (circulatory) – helps to promote the elasticity of tissues. Tongue**: hard, cracked or flabby. Cold sores of the mouth. **Discharge:** Lumpy, yellow, thick. **Ulcers & Fistula:** Thick yellow pus. **Menses:** Flooding during period. Piles and varicose veins.

- **Calc. Phos – anabolic (to build up) – helps to strengthen the bones, building new blood cells.** **Tongue:** bad, disgusting taste in the morning. Tongue swollen and blistered. Decaying teeth. **Discharges:** Like an egg white. Indigestion, chilblains, low vitality.

- **Calc. Sulph. – pus/inflammation – acts as a purifier.** Speeds up slow healing of skin and wounds. **Tongue:** coated as if with dry clay, taste sometimes soapy. Spots in teenagers and sore lips.

- **Ferrum Phos. – for fever** (in first aid; tongue fairly clean) – helps distribute oxygen in the body. **Colds:** just after getting chilled. **Bleeding/Haemorrhages**, bright red blood, fresh wounds. Nose bleeding. Sore throat, coughs, chestiness. Muscular rheumatism.

- **Kali Mur. – first inflammation – tonsillitis, bronchitis, sore throat, catarrh and colds. Herpes lips. Tongue:** white/greyish, with blisters or ulcers. Sluggish digestion.

- **Kali Phos. – nerves (backache, halitosis. helps to reduce fever) – headaches, depression. Diarrhoea**, with painless thin stools. **Dysentery** with putrid bloody stool. **Tongue:** brownish.

- **Kali Sulph. – for metabolism – promotes and maintains healthy skin.** **Tongue:** yellow, slimy. Insipid taste or loss. Nails and hair in poor condition. **Discharge:** Slimy or greenish.

- **Mag. Phos. – cramps! – Nerves and muscle fibre nutrient.** **Tongue:** generally clean, whitish in diarrhoea. **Menses:** Dark flow and **painful**. Acute spasm, hiccups, colic and wind. Use to relieve <u>darting pains.</u>

- **Nat. Mur. – controls the distribution of water/fluids in the body.** **Tongue:** salty taste, frothy saliva or dry tongue. **Catarrh:** thin watery discharge, with loss of taste and smell. From all mucous membrane there is excessive thin watery secretion, flow of tears, runny nose etc.

- **Nat. Phos. – neutralises acids (anti-acids) – acid-alkaline regulator of the cells.** **Tongue:** moist, creamy, coating at the back of tongue. Acid or coppery taste. **Perspiration:** Sour smelling. **Heartburns**, gastric indigestions and rheumatic pains.

- **Nat. Sulph. – detoxification** (Glauber's salt: destroys bacteria & viruses) – balances body fluids. **Tongue:** greenish, brown or grey coating. Burning blisters on the tip of tongue. **Generally:** biliousness, green discharges. **Menses:** profuse with diarrhoea in the morning. **Morning sickness**, digestive problems, bilious attack, headaches. Influenza.

- **Silicea. – for connective tissue – conditioner and cleanser, eliminates waste.** **Pus/inflammation**, pimples, boils, spots and styes. **Tongue:** indurations and ulcers. **Piles:** painful, fistula anus. **Discharge:** offensive, thick yellow, hepatic eruptions around nostrils.

ARIES – the Ram

21st March – 20th April
Kali Phosphoricum
(Phosphate of Potassium)
Planet Mars

Aries is a 'Fire' sign and is often described as the most forceful and competitive of all the star signs. They like to 'show off' and want all luxuries in life, often wasting their money in this way, wanting to be number ONE. As well as 'willpower' they usually have a very good memory.

Hahnemann certainly was an Aries, being born on 10th April. Reading books about his life one could agree with some of the above mentioned qualities. He preached in what he believed with 'assertiveness', not being swayed by the critics. He was true to his birth sign, an enterprising 'free spirit', bossy and opinionated, yet confident that Homœopathy was the way for the future to help people overcome their dis-ease. Hahnemann was also very warm-hearted and humble at times and reading anecdotes about him shows what a great soul he was.

Let us study this sign from a spiritual point of view: **Aries** is the <u>first sign of the Zodiac</u>, commencing on the first day of Spring with the **Spring Equinox** (equinox meaning equal) and bringing an awakening of nature; the RESURRECTION! Although **Aries** starts in **March** (on **21st**) let us look at the meaning of **APRIL**, which comes from the **Latin 'APERIO'** meaning 'to **uncover**', to render accessible. **Aries is** the first male sign of the Zodiac and is ruled by Mars, which is presented by the **Pineal gland**, while the **Pituitary** is ruled by the **Moon (female energy)**. These two constitute the male and female, which God joined together in the 'Garden of Eden'. **Aries** is associated with the **CEREBRUM**, <u>the God</u> brain; the word **cere-brum** comes from '**cere**' meaning WAX.

Aries the **RAM** comes from Sanskrit, meaning '**HIGH**', the top of the head. In Hebrew the most high means **CALVARY** (or Golgotha), **the Place of Ascension!** (Also known as 'SKULL HILL'.) In order to '**ascend**' our chemical electricity must be in balance, i.e. must match the **Cosmic** electricity! (<u>See Libra, the 'scales' and opposite sign of Aries.</u>) The cell salts can help to solve the problem of how to go about it. The tissue salt for Aries is Kali-Phosphoricum.

Kali-p. stimulates the **Nerve Power** and acts as the '**vehicles of consciousness**'. (While **Mag.-Phos.** is the '**moving salt**' and **Calc-f.** is the '**builder**', **Kali-p.** is the **electricity** and the 'spark of life'). **Kali-p.** produces the <u>highest rate of vibration of the 12 basic minerals</u> in the body.

KALI is the Sanskrit word for FIRE. The Hindu goddess **Kali** is the powerful deity in Nature for Fire and in the older Vedic form the word **Alkali** was Father and Mother, or positive and negative combined in harmony. (**AL or EL is Hebrew** for **GOD or father**.) If we consider that our food is now more than 60% acid forming leaves at best only 40% to help the body to remain in harmony between acid and alkaline, we can see how important these tissue salts can be. Most scientists would agree that there can be no life without **Potassium**!

Potassium is a soft, brilliant, bluish-white metal melting at 62° Celsius into a liquid resembling <u>Mercury (the messenger of the gods)</u>. **Potassium** thrown in water instantly creates a powerful electrical current, catches fire and burns with its <u>characteristic violet flame</u>! (Remember the wavelength of the colour violet at 380 nm, the only range the carcinogens reacted to in Prof. Popp's research). <u>There can be no life without FIRE</u> as it **creates, destroys** and **preserves**.

111

Chemically speaking the tissue salts will help create this daily bread from **heaven** (= *the skull*) to come down **to Earth, to** *the torso/body*. If the right chemical exchange is **not** taking place the body becomes a **graveyard,** with too many dead bodies/corpuscles!

TAURUS – the Bull

21st April – 21st May
Natrum Sulphuricum
(Sulphate of Sodium)
Planet Venus

Taurus is an 'Earth' sign and is well known for stubbornness, as well as being traditional and hard working. The Taurean will enjoy beautiful things around them, like money and possessions, and can get a bit selfish about them. They also have a love for rich foods, which often causes them health problems in later life. At times they can be a bit boring due to grumpiness, being very habit-bound and sticking to clichés, but at the same time the honesty and faithfulness makes them trustworthy friends to have around.

Taurus is the **second sign** of the Zodiac and was once worshipped as the **'healing god'**. With spring in the air, the weather naturally getting warmer and the soil becoming ready for planting, people too were positive after the harsh winter months and metaphorically speaking were at this time 'growing in strength'. This growing in strength also points to the Sun, which gets stronger at this time of year (April/May), and with this comes healing. In fact 'HELIOS' the SUN, or Apollo to the Greeks, was the giver of life, light and heat.

While Aries was associated with the cerebrum (the main mass of the brain) **Taurus is associated with the cerebellum,** which is the **animal brain** or **subconscious**. This is situated at the back of the skull behind the brainstem. As it is the 'sub-conscious' it means that it is 'under' the MOST HIGH and is ruled by the 'animal passion'! Here we must view the opposite of **Taurus**, its complement **SCORPIO**, where the animal mind finds its expression! **Taurus the Bull** ploughs the earth preparing for the seeds that the 'Adam-man' will sow. However, what will the ground be like? Will it be fertile or barren? **Taurus** must be 'yoked' and guided by wisdom.

Those born under **Taurus** are 'Lymphatic Types' and can easily be negative if you consider the picture of **Nat-s.**, which is the tissue salt here. They love their food, thus become easily overweight and increase in size even if on a strict diet and this creates acids in the body, which is very unhealthy. **Nat-s.** is said to be the 'reducing' agent, helping to reduce the 'running wild' aspect of behaviour and out of control e-motions! As mentioned before the real function is **MOTION, not E-MOTIONS**, which are the thieves that rob us our energy. **Nat-s.** is electro-negative, is linked to sodium, and is especially active in **water**. Thus it is the ideal salt to help reduce weight by attracting waste products in the body, which are found in the fluids.

If the lymphatic system is engorged, humidity and moisture in the air makes life even more difficult (no good living in the tropics). When the blood becomes overcharged with water, the various tissues must suffer from lack of nourishment and the corpuscles are literally 'drowned'; the person will thus suffer 'drowsiness'. (Sleeping sickness is the worst form of this.)

The Cerebellum is primarily concerned with posture, balance and the coordination of movement. Any damage or disease would result in slurred speech, a staggering gait and other uncoordinated movements. Alcohol intoxication can impair the function of the cerebellum, which is not able to control the complex task of co-ordinating the nerve impulses underlying the muscular activity. In this case the remedy 'Sulphuric acid' should be considered in order to lessen the disease 'alcoholism' and the desire for 'having a drink'. Nat-s. may also be given as support to feed the starving cells in this part of the brain. An unhealthy, deficient brain that has been poisoned with waste products is unable to produce harmonious or balanced thoughts. **Nat-s.** is also well known to work well for **head injuries** and in cases of **epilepsy after head injury**, as well as **spinal meningitis** from clinical experiences.

The nerve fluids of the **Pineal** and **Pituitary** glands *cross* over at the point/place in the head where **Taurus, the cerebellum begins**; known as the 'Cross on Golgotha'. This is the **cross** on which animal nature brings suffering! The nerves not only cross at the base of the brain, but also at the **2nd Lumbar Vertebra** (in the sign of **Scorpio**). The left and right sympathetic systems are the 'thieves' as they control the **E-Motions**, and until these are under control a depletion of the tissue salt (**Nat-s.**) will take place.

Natrum Sulphuricum was first discovered in 1658 by the alchemist Glauber (1604-1668) and we still call it by his name 'Glauber's Salt'. Apart from using it to nurture the brain it is very much a liver remedy. It is therefore also aptly called 'the cleanser', as love for rich food or too much food 'living in the land of plenty' can be used for daily detoxification. Once the liver is less toxic 'addictive eating patterns' will naturally be lowered. This can be of great use to Taureans, as the organs of weakness for this sign are the liver and gallbladder, plus ears, neck and throat, face and lower jaw. **Sulphur** is an essential chemical of human/animal tissue (as well as plant life) that we obtain from food. It is the only visible **chemical found in protein**.

In **Sanskrit** the month of **May** is written **'mag'**, which means **'move'**, and we still dance/move around the May-pole as a sign of celebrating MAY. The word **Maia**, who was the 'queen of heaven', derives from the same root word and in ancient times she offered gifts on the first day of May.

GEMINI – the Twins

22nd May – 21st June
Kali Muriaticum
(Chloride of Potassium)
Planet Mercury

Gemini is an 'Air' sign from which we have versatility, fast thinking, fast talking and sharp wittedness. However, there are two of them; these twins are almost like 'quicksilver' (mercury) and alternate rapidly, moving from one thing to another, rather superficially. Generally speaking they keep a large circle of friends, yet can easily upset 'emotionally sensitive' people with their 'clever talking'. Communication is their strong point and being very inquisitive they are always on the look out for new ideas and are fascinated by facts.

Gemini, the twins, is the third sign of the Zodiac and signifies the lower and higher self. The ruler of this star sign is **Mercury, the 'Messenger of the Gods'**. Here the messenger is in the form of <u>physio-chemical electricity</u> that carries the energy of life up **the NERVES; 'up the tree' of life**. If this 'spinning salt' is lacking <u>man is crucified on the tree</u>, since the two nervous systems constitute this living **'TREE'**. The winged pole of Mercury symbolises this **'tree of life'**, which the serpent, or Kundalini energy, coiled at the base of the spine corresponds to. This is also referred to as the **'tree of knowledge of good and evil'**. We all carry this tree of life within. (Wings are the symbol of the 'divine mission'.)

The Twins are supposed to work in harmony; one represents the **'sensory system'** and the other the **'motor'**, so one **does the work** the other the **motions**. The nerves join with their fine branches, like a fine **'spider-web' connecting** the head to the body. Messages are carried by electrical impulses propagating along the nerve fibres. These nerve fibres can of course be damaged by infection or inflammation, or through poisoning (environmental toxins), metabolic disorders or nutritional deficiencies. If the chemical formulae of the brain and nerves are not perfect it is not possible to have absolute self control. When Kali-m. is present the **positive mind expands**, helping us to think faster and more clearly, whereas if it is in short supply, the **negative mind stagnates** and the spinning process has stopped. The fibres can get congested and swell as the blood thickens. Therefore the heart has to work harder and the thinking becomes slow and dull; the threads have broken. The spider web referred to above, or **'spinning'** in the body, is done by:

KALI MURIATICUM – The 'SPINNING SALT'

Kali Mur. provides the 'fibrin' (fibre) necessary for the formation of nerves, ligaments, veins, skin, tissue, and in fact all flesh. It effectively weaves the seamless garment for the flesh of the body. The month of **June** in Latin means **'join'** or **'joining'** and the saying 'PHYSICIAN HEAL THYSELF' could be the way we want to think about this spinning salt of Kali Mur.

Kali Muriaticum never had a 'proving'. From the work of Dr Schuessler, however, we have plenty of information of its use through clinical experience and his teachings: "It is contained in nearly all the cells and is chemically related to fibrin. It will dissolve white and greyish-white secretions of the mucous membrane and plastic exudation". It can deal with 'ill effects of vaccination', cuts, blows and burns to the body. It is interesting to note that in the **Mind Section** of this remedy we find: **'Patient imagines he must starve'**. He is discontented and discouraged and his mind is picking up what is lacking in the body where vital repair work to the nerves is not taking place, since the 'spinning has stopped'.

You will remember that the **Caduceus,** the symbol of the medical profession, also represents the lower body being connected to the upper body. The verb **'cado'** in Latin means **'fall'** thus the Caduceus is to be interpreted as the 'fall from heaven' leaving a **cadaver**, which is derived from the same root word: No wonder the patient fears evil and starvation!

In mythology Jupiter was the father of **Mercury**, who is the patron of merchants and thieves, as well as he who conducts the souls of the dead to the lower worlds. The cerebro-spinal fluid/substance is the creative essence often called the **'Manna from Heaven'** or the **'Elixir of Life',** or even the **'Ambrosia of the Gods'**. By not nurturing this 'electrical energy' rightly with tissue salts, metaphysically speaking we become the 'thieves' of God's merchandise in our body.

In the Vedas **the TWINS** were called the **'Physicians of Heaven'** and in classical mythology they are represented as the twin sons of Jupiter and Leda by **two planets** by the names of **CASTOR & POLLUX** where they were worshipped as gods and finally place in the constellation of Gemini. The word **Castus** in Latin means **pure, spotless, abstinent** from sensual **pleasures, and chastity**, while the word **Pollux** means **pollute!** The twin brothers live alternately, one during daytime, representing the higher mind and living a life that leads to illumination, and the other appears only at night-time, symbolising 'spiritual' darkness. (Most of the human race lives out this shadow side of the spirit, in the lower mind.) Another Latin derivation also says that *polluere* means to *'wash forth',* while **LUX** means light, so all is not lost!

CANCER – the Crab

22nd June – 23rd July
Calcium Fluoratum
(Fluoride of Lime)
The Moon

Cancer is the forth sign of the Zodiac (opposite Capricorn) and a 'Water' sign. Emotionally they are very sensitive, sentimental and romantic. Their moods can wax and wane like the **Moon**, which is their celestial body. Mothering and protection is 'built into' this sign, as its focus is on the home, the roots, and the family. There is a need for privacy in Cancerians and the link to the past is strong, which is the basis for new growth. Cancer under the Moon is a very good sign for nurturing the intuition. With their love of security in relationships and finance they are very empathetic to others not fortunate enough to enjoy what is so important to them.

During the time of **Cancer** the **Sun** is at its highest in the Northern Hemisphere at the time of the **Solstice**, yet this sign is **ruled by the Moon**. This signifies the '**lower**' mind, as is stated in the **Upanishad**: '**The Sun is Spirit, matter is the Moon**'! (Spirit is the father energy, matter is the mother energy.)

The organ associated with this sign is the **SPLEEN**, which again is **female energy**. Other organs related to the star sign Cancer are the **breasts** (very female and very nurturing), and the **stomach and gastric tract**, which nurture the 'self' with food.

The secret of **Cancer** is to reproduce; this is nature at its best, **recreating itself daily**. Yet **here we do** not mean re-creation with pro-creation seeds, rather the ceaseless renewal of the **blood corpuscles** in the spleen. The female energy helps this **FLOW**, like the ebb and flow of the tides. (Like the menstrual cycle, influenced by the moon.) In order to rejuvenate and reproduce itself the body needs:

CALCIUM FLUOR, or FLUX – (Fluoride of Lime)

By giving Calc-f. as a low potency we supplement the work of nature and do not work against it. This salt is also known as the 'natural flux'. As a tissue salt Calc-f. is also known as Schuessler's **bone salt** as it is found on the surface of bones and on the enamel of teeth. The word **Fluor** stems for the Latin word **Fluo**, meaning **to flow**! However, it also has the root in **fluorescent**: 'it glows on exposure to moderate heat'.

In **Egypt** the '**crab**' was symbolised by the **Scarabaeus**, the dung beetle. It is still the most popular souvenir from Egypt, where it has always been used as an amulet. In Ancient Egypt it was placed over the heart during mummification to ensure a safe passage to the underworld. The Scarab or Scarabaeus stands for resurrection and rebirth; immortality, to BUILD AGAIN.

Cancer the crab belongs to the family of **Crustacean**, which in Greek means 'crystal', giving us the picture of crystallisation or hardening, like the enamel on teeth and strong nails. If Calc-f. is deficient in the body, nails break, teeth crumble, and the skin gets rough, chaps and cracks in the corner of month. Furthermore the tongue has a cracked appearance, the skin at the back of the ears is broken, and even worse and more painful are anal fissures.

Lack of this salt also causes varicose veins and a general 'sagging down' as it is found in all connective tissue and elastic fibres of all muscle tissue. This lack of muscle tone can show up with a prolapsed uterus or a prolapsed transverse colon, as is so often seen in the iris. On the other hand there can be bone spurs, swellings and indurations and easy dislocation of joints.

The earliest symptom that Calc-f. is lacking is **FORGETFULNESS**! The person searches for words, and repeats, hesitates and searches for answers. They have _'cobwebs on the brain'_: This cobweb, or 'spider-web-like' membrane, is a fine serous membrane. It is the middle one of the three enveloping the brain and spinal cord, and this connective tissue is also found between cerebrum and the cerebellum. You can see that if this is <u>not</u> strong enough they **'fear financial ruin'**, and a groundless 'fear of financial loss' is in the **Mind** rubric of this remedy. **'Fear of poverty'** encourages the crab to hold on to every cent. The mental condition can be one of depression, anxiety and indecision.

As mentioned earlier Calc-f. works on the stomach and gastric tract, as these are ruled by **Cancer**. Thus, flatulence, acute indigestion from fatigue, and brain fag have been helped with Calc-f., as well as vomiting of undigested food in infants and 'nausea and distress from eating'. 65% of people born under the sign of Cancer are 'weaklings' and undernourished at birth. Nevertheless, despite looking very delicate they can be surprisingly strong.

LEO – the Lion

24th July – 23rd August
Magnesium Phosphoricum
(Phosphate of Magnesia)
The SUN

Leo is the second 'Fire' sign after Aries, full of pride in achievements. People born under this sign can be over-bearing attention seekers, yet make natural leaders. The fire they have within kindles great creativity, enjoyment in life, hobbies, children and love affairs. **Leo** is fifth sign and the only **BEAST** in the Zodiac, representing the '**king of the beasts on Earth**'. They want to be admired and flattered, and dominate those around them. They do not easily forget kindness done to them, are loyal and their devotion is endless. Often they are blessed with an enormous amount of energy. During this hottest time of the year (from 24th July to 23rd August) everything ripens by the energy (heat and light) from the Sun, which comes to its peak in these months. This energy includes the passion of the **animal heat** for **pro-creation** and thus we have sexual passion, love affairs, and amusement. **Leo** the animal is the beast within.

LEO is the '**lord of all**' and is ruled by the **SUN**. It is opposite Aquarius and is the real man, the regenerated being. While Aries is the place of sowing, Leo is the place of reaping; we have to secure that the fruits we reap are not a poison. Toxic waste products within can 'consume' the body and these poisonous wastes can be created by 'ill' emotions that consume us. As the ruler is the **Sun**, the metal is **Gold**, and since 'pure' gold does not oxidise or burn its essence was the 'yang' of Eastern philosophies, while silver was 'yin' (the female essence). The organs assigned to this sign are of course the **Heart** (of gold), the **Spine** and the **Back**. The tissue salt is:

Phosphate of Magnesia, the 'MOVING SALT'

Schuessler stated that Mag-p. is contained in the blood corpuscles, muscles, brain, spinal marrow, nerves and teeth. Disturbance of its molecules results not only in 'pain', but in **cramps and paralysis**. The disturbance is so great that the sufferers 'talk about their pains all the time'. There is dullness and an inability to think clearly, and certainly an indisposition to study or do any mental work. If any such activity is tried drowsiness puts an immediate stop to it again. They become very forgetful and mental depression and anxiety follow; this not at all the picture of a proud Lion!

Leo stands for **MOTION** and from **Magnesium** we have the root word '**mag**', which in Sanskrit means to '**move**'. **Magnesium** possesses the property of being repelled by a magnet and repelling can also be translated as 'being moved'. An old saying tells us that 'if you do not move it, you lose it', thus this tissue salt will help to keep everything moving nicely. The picture of Mag-p. tells us that if the movement stops then the cramps will start. Angina Pectoris (spasms of the heart) can be helped greatly by this tissue salt; dissolve Mag. Phos. in warm water and drink slowly.

These heart spasms are intensified when acid is present in the body for a long time, as acids will attract magnesium. They are also made worse if Silicea is either deficient or almost not present at all in the body. Silicea is the tissue salt for the next 'Fire' sign, Sagittarius (but more about that later).

The pains associated with **Mag-p.** are 'shooting like lightning' and it is **interesting** to note that if magnesium is heated it will burn with a dazzling light! (Phosphorus and Hydrogen also have the same properties.) **Lock jaw, spasmodic coughing, choking, sneezing, hiccough, and cramps in fingers and neck/legs all call for this remedy.** There is also a special affinity with **CALCIUM**, which can be given in combination with **Mag-p.** Another <u>combination for loss of smell</u>, for example, would require **Mag-p.** and other salts in combination: **Nat Mur. + Nat-s.+ Calc. Sulph.**

VIRGO – the Virgin

24th August – 23rd September
Kali Sulphuricum
(Potassium Sulphate)
Planet Earth

VIRGO is an 'Earth' sign and although it seems to be female, it is in fact neuter; thus the barren Earth! But let us look at the qualities first: Their approach to life is very methodical and meticulous, yet practical in an 'earthy' way. They can be critical and narrow-minded at times but probably the best word to summarise them is 'perfectionist'! They like to be of service to others, even to the extent where it can be detrimental to their own health. This may be expressed as ulcers in the **intestine** and the lower abdomen, which are their 'weak' organs. Here the Bowel Nosodes, as well as Carcinosin, will serve them well, making sure that they not to become a 'doormat' for the rest of the family or community. Incidentally, the word **Intestine** means 'within' or 'inside'. If the human intestine were to be fully stretched out it would be six times longer than the body itself! The star constellation in the sky allocated to this part of the anatomy is the **Great Dragon or Hydra**! (Is this the hundred-headed-Hydra that Hahnemann referred to when talking about **Psora**, the **MOTHER** of all **Dis-eases** and the great dragon within?)

Continuing with looking at the importance of words I would like you to consider the words implicated with Virgo, the Mother: The Latin word for **Virgin** translates to **Divine Mother** (Virgin Mary). The Hebrew letter **M** is spelt **MEM** and in the ancient language stood for **mother**. It also means **material** (the substance from which we are made), and **magnetic** (which is needed to keep us 'grounded' on Earth). (In physics the M-theory – where the M stands for membrane – is the name associated with investigating possibilities of 'Parallel Universes', which I found fascinating when watching a television programme on the BBC recently.)

An old English word for **marrow** was **MARY** and we are aware that **marrow** fills the bones and contains **95 % FAT**. The 'lamp' that the virgin has to light is the **cerebrum** (in Aries the most high), but until the spinal oil is sufficiently refined it cannot burn brightly. **Oil** is therefore the 'lubricator' of man's machinery. In old age when the body is low of oil the skin looks dry and shrivelled. But what is missing, apart from oil? The explanation can be found in another word: The French call sea 'Mar' (in German it is called 'Meer') and the mother 'Mere'. Both of these words have a connection with the sea from which we came; even when we are in the uterus we are bathed in the amniotic fluid and feel secure, like a fish in the sea. This leads us to the next Tissue Salt:

Kali Sulphuricum – the 'OIL' to lubricate

The oceans contain enormous quantities of **Potassium Sulphate (Kali-s.)**. Other well known sea remedies are **AMBER** (the fossil resin) by the name of Succinum, as well as **AMBERGRIS** (the excretion from the alimentary canal of the sperm whale), and it has been established that these 'hardened' oils are 'highly electric'. **Potassium**, you will remember, is **the alkali of the body** and in combination with Sulphur this forms **oil** or **Kali-s.**

To **Schuessler** Kali-s. was his '**Pulsatilla**', which could be used everyday to bring about the changes needed to restore health. If this tissue salt is deficient the person will **feel suffocated** and will be **very sensitive to atmospheric** conditions and changes, just like Pulsatilla. Kali-s. works very well with Ferrum (iron) since combustion cannot take place without sufficient oxygen (and as we will see later, Ferrum Phosphoricum is found in Pisces, which is the opposite of Virgo and Kali-s.)

Virgo is the sixth month of the Zodiac and the **'House of Health'!** Health is present when all chemical constituents of the blood are present, which is not easy to achieve in a world full of toxins. Good health also means being **PURE** and **PERFECT**, and not adulterated! The word **ADULT** has the same root as 'adulteration' and should mean 'one who has attained full size and strength; grown into **maturity**'! Have all the souls really reached maturity over the aeons of time, or are they stuck in a childish/adolescent behaviour most of the time? The 7th Commandment tells us that **'Thou shalt not commit adultery'!** So what is going wrong when the body is abused in a variety of ways?

'The Serpent beguiled me and I did eat', said **EVE. Eve** in **Hebrew** means **LIFE**, but because of **'beguilement'**, 'life' from the spiritual point of view was lost due to the hypnotic power of **SEX.** This was the departure from the **Garden of Eden**, leaving the place where perfect health, happiness and peace existed. 'Heal' also means to be **MADE WHOLE** or **HOLY**, but we cannot HEAL (the patient) unless they heal themselves from within. Kali-s. can be one of the ways to replace what is missing.

When crystallising this salt forms a beautiful **double six-sided Pyramid** (again giving us the magical figure of 12). The vibration of **Kali Sulph. moves in a circle** like a spinning top or magical wheel; the wheel of life, giving back time, not immortality to the physical body, but 'lubrication' to 'keep going', when it would otherwise cease to exist.

Although like other tissue salts Kali-s. never had a formal proving, the **'Mind'** section tells us that the patient 'feels always in a hurry'. There is a desire to lie down, but lying down aggravates so this person 'must walk for relief'. They have desires – all the same reject things as mental exertion aggravates, they give up before they try. Like a machine lacking the oil, it wants to go but cannot. **All discharges are profuse and deep yellow, which is a leading symptom.**

Coming back to the **intestine** (which is the organ in question here), part of this is located in the **SOLAR PLEXUS** and can be called the **SUN PLEXUS**, which is located at the back of the stomach and is the seat of **Feelings and Sensations.** From the solar plexus twelve different nerve ganglia branch off in all directions. Each one of the twelve divisions is allocated to one of the twelve signs of the zodiac and represents a **SPOKE OF THE HUB**, all of which combined give us the physical **'Wheel of Life'.** (Thus like a little Zodiac).

When saying 'I love you with all my heart' it would be more appropriate to say 'I love you with all my bowels'; of course this is far less attractive, yet the bowels are the organ allocated to **Virgo** and no doubt most people are familiar with having a **'gut feeling'** about something (butterflies in the stomach). Even in the Scriptures we find the saying: 'Jacob's **bowels** yearned after his son'! The **Solar Plexus is the broadcasting station,** sending forth and receiving messages to the rest of the body.

With the **age of Aquarius** now upon us, all the poisons that the body takes in on a daily basis in terms of 'consuming materials', i.e. alcohol, tobacco, drugs and animal meat, will lessen and gradually disappear. This way we can keep the **'fire of the temple always burning',** as the **virgins** are supposed to be the **'custodians of the sacred fire'.** A fire was always lit at the Spring Equinox, in Aries. Let us work together to reach this goal and keep the lamps burning to be the light in the dark to help those around us. This brings us back to Virgo and wanting to serve others.

A few more indications here as to when Kali-s. should be given:

- **Shifting pains is also a sign of lack of this salt,** which can assist in promotion of perspiration, thus should be given freely for colds/catarrhal conditions of the head/ears/eyes; sticky yellow green, like Pulsatilla. < heated atmosphere, > cool air.
- Dread of hot drinks, and thirst-less.
- **Hot Flushes** (< afternoon/early evening) and the desire for cold air, experienced by females during menopause when lacking in **Kali-s.**
- **Skin problems** in all children's diseases involving the skin, in order to aid formation of new skin.

LIBRA – the Scales

24th September – 23rd October
Natrum Phosphoricum
(Phosphate of Sodium)
Planet Venus

Libra is the second 'Air' sign after Gemini, and this shows at times when they cannot make up their mind which 'way the wind is blowing'. Apart from indecisiveness, they display fairness and want harmony. Everything needs to be in 'balance' and thus they strive for justice and listen to other people's arguments in order not to hurt anyone's feelings. If at all possible Librans avoid problems; rather than dealing with them they hope the problems will go away. Generally speaking they are very charming, have an excellent taste and are in need of a partner, as friendship and marriage is greatly valued by them. These peace-loving people make good diplomats.

Libra is the 7th sign of the Zodiac and is opposite Aries. When we add up the number of signs we have from the beginning so far, including Libra, we arrive at the number **8** and thus we have **2 scales of equal number; 4+4 = a square** for each scale to bring about **'balance'**. The right side of the scale represent the first six signs, while the left pan covers the last six signs. Libra represents the **7th day,** which is the day of rest, the **Lord's Day**. Nature needs to rest too, to regain balance. While **ARIES** is the positive end of the pole, **LIBRA** is the negative. The Latin word for **scale is 'Pound'** and of course we use the pound to measure things, in Britain even in terms of money. (To 'weigh up' is to consider if it is worth the money, or as an old saying goes 'worth its weight in gold!')

The Planet for Libra is **Venus**, meaning **Material**, which is associated with the autumn harvest time (Psoric Miasm). The opposite of Libra is **Aries**, which is ruled by **Mars** (the opposite of Venus) and Mars represents the **renewed Energy** of springtime (Sycotic Miasm), which is a time of the year when everything comes back to life after the hibernation of winter (Tubercular Miasm).

A little more information about mythology: **Venus** was the Roman Goddess of beauty and sensual love, and is identified with Aphrodite. She had a son by Mercury called **Cupid,** meaning **'desire',** or known as **Eros** in Greek mythology. Now, Cupid shoots **'darts'** at people to 'catch them off guard' and have them lust or long for on another. Venus' chief festival day is 1st April, or April Fool's day, which you will notice is during the reign of Aries. **Venus** is the 'brightly shining' star you will see first thing in the evening and the last one to disappear in the morning; it is known as the **Morning Star,** but also as **Lucifer** (from the Latin for 'light bearer'). If you are beginning to wonder what Venus and Cupid shooting his darts has to do with our tissue salt, here is one interpretation. **Acid** in Latin derives from **ACIDUS**, meaning sharp cutting! Venus must ask her son CUPID to throw away his darts (the 'sharp cuttings') in order to be in balance again, which is expressed in Libra as the scales, and the tissue salt to help here is:

Natrum Phosphoricum the 'NEUTRALISING' Salt

Nat. Phos is best known to **neutralise acids** and thus may be called the **'balancing'** salt. The Latin word for salt is **natrum or natron**, which belongs to the root word **'niteo'** and translates into 'bright, shiny, glittering' and splendid. **'NITRO'** means to rest and to attain equilibrium; one must be **'still'** and **rest.**

The organs associated with this sign are the **Kidneys, Adrenal Glands** and the **Bladder**. (Incidentally, no vital organ will be found in the next five Zodiac signs.) Nat-p. is to be used when the urine is too acidic, causing burning during very frequent urination. It will help to make the urine more alkaline again. **Acidity** within produces 'sour belching', 'canker sores of lips and cheeks', everything will be 'worse for acid forming food'.

The tongue will have a creamy yellow coating, especially at the base. This 'sourness' can already be detected in babies, especially when bottle fed, when they do not thrive and vomit 'sour cheesy masses'. If not 'neutralised' these acid conditions sadly provide a 'good home' for threadworms in children, which is another reason to cleanse the bowels with the Nosodes and support it with tissue salts. Otherwise a mental weakness may develop, with nervousness and forgetfulness, as well as being frightened easily with **'fears'** especially at night and **'worrying'** that something will happen. And this is all too true; something really will happen if this tissue salt is 'out of balance' and diseases will follow suit!

SCORPIO – the Scorpion

24th October – 22nd November
Calcarea Sulphurica
(Sulphate of Lime)
Planet Mars/Pluto

Scorpio is the eighth sign of the Zodiac that the Sun enters on 24th October, and is another 'Water' sign. Here we have a person who can be very sexy, secretive, intense and obsessive. They can be very direct in their approach, yet with great charisma and personal magnetism. Scorpio can have a deadly sting in the tail so be sure not to cross their path in a way that you undermine their authority, as they are passionate about their desires. Sadly, most of them do not easily forget or forgive, yet due to great strength within can also endure more than others. The ruler of this sign is **MARS**, the same as for **Aries**.

Scorpio is in the 9th Month of the astrological year, which is the month of death when we celebrate 'All Saints day' and 'Remembrance Day'. According to an old Dutch word 'slagth-maand' this month was known as the slaughter month. One could argue that this was the time of year when the beast was 'slain' (killed and salted, to be preserved for the winter months). The sign of Scorpio was also considered the very **'gate of Hell'**, as the five cold winter months were to follow, although on the other hand Scorpio was not always associated with this month. The ancient sign was the **EAGLE**, giving hope that not all is lost as the **Eagle is a symbol for 'life everlasting'**. (They used to let an eagle fly from the funeral pyre of a deceased emperor, symbolising the reception of his soul amongst the gods.)

Halloween, which is celebrated on 31st October, is not a 'modern' idea of dressing up and playing 'spooks' but was celebrated in ancient times when **ghosts, witches, goblins** and **evil spirits** were to be driven out. On the **1st November** the **Druids** in England held their great **autumn festival**, when fires were lit in honour of the Sun-god to give thanks for the harvest. As Aries and Scorpio are both ruled by Mars, it has to be considered that on one hand there is Aries being positive, while on the other hand **Scorpio** is viewed as the negative (the Angel of Death). Remember the 'sting in the tail' trying to foster the beast in men, which in the Bible is mentions in Revelation 9:5 that 'their torment was the torment of a scorpion, when it striketh a man'. The scorpion was the symbol of evil and because of the treachery of its bite became the symbol of Judas.

The heavenly picture of Scorpio includes two stars by the name of 'caput gallinaginis', which in Latin means **'head of the woodcock'** and in physiological terms stands for the ejaculating glands. The cock is the most magnetic and electric of all birds, thus the Greek name is **'Electrum'**. It has become a symbol of 'Passion', based upon Christ's response to Peter's avowal of loyalty: 'Verily, verily, I say unto thee, the cock shall not crow till thou hast denied me thrice' (John 13:38).

Harmony and balance found in **Libra** must be achieved between **Virgo** and **Scorpio** to turn Scorpio into the **'White Eagle'** it once was; the symbol of resurrection. The eagle is supposed to have the ability to soar up high until lost out of sight, not blinded even by the mid-day Sun. For this reason it came to symbolise Christ and stands for virtues of courage, faith and contemplation.

Regarding the **organs** allocated to **Scorpio**, the genitals are **'solely for procreation'**. These organs are located at the base of the spine where the coiled up serpent, the Kundalini (Sanskrit for 'the coil in the hair off the beloved) is also sited. In Isaiah a direct reference to **Scorpio** as the **flying serpent** is *'for out of the serpent's root shall come forth a cockatrice and his fruit shall be a fiery flying serpent'*.

The word **Adam** in Hebrew means '**red earth**' (the colour of the flesh) and remember **Earth** is the meaning for **SALT**, thus the BIBLE states that God made man from the **DUST** of the **Earth**'. In Genesis the statement 'multiply, replenish and subdue to EARTH' does not refer to pro-creation, but to 'renew' one's own body and overcome our animal side. The tissue salt allocated to this sign is:

Calcium Sulphurica – the 'Plaster of Paris' or 'Gypsum'

The action of this tissue salt, which has been proved by Constantin Hering, is very similar to Hepar Sulphurica, although is not as sensitive to the environment. While Hep-sulph. does not like the slightest exposure to air, Calc-s. is better in open air and has a desire for it. The tendency to **Suppuration** is the main theme. It was Schuessler's connective tissue remedy.

This salt is very much needed in **venereal diseases; Kali-mur.** the 'spinning salt' is the other. **Infertility** in both male and female requires **Calc. Sulph.** to get rid of possible 'pus' in the reproductive system and to restore 'strong' casts/cells for the seeds. Both creative and procreative corpuscles need this salt. Additionally, without enough of this salt the coating of the stomach would become thin, with ulcers resulting very quickly. This is one of the modalities: '**Burning sensation**'.

Even the skin might have the burning sensation, thus Calc. Sulph. is very useful as an eczema remedy, with burning feet, like Sulphur. The **eyeballs, nasal passage, mouth, throat** and **oesophagus, stomach** and **bladder** all need this salt for **protection**.

Anaemia is a lack of Calcium Sulphurica and yellowish and pasty coloured skin, often with unhealthy skin, pimples and pustules are part of this remedy picture, as well as painful fistula, or abscesses about the anus.

A closer look at the second name, **Plaster of Paris,** reveals that when this salt is mixed with water the water will quickly evaporate. This leads to the formation of the '**plaster**' we know as '**Gypsum**', the other name, suggesting that the second label has its root in **GYPSY**. In this case, the word is not of Latin origin, rather from the East meaning 'to wander without fixed purpose', or 'to go round' or equally to '**Gyrate**'. The Latin equivalent word is NOMAS, which is the need to 'distribute'. We must remember that the cerebral fluid 'gyrates' in a figure of eight. All energy is constantly in motion and in order for the body to renew itself everything needs to 'gyrate'.

Alabaster is the most beautiful form of **Calc-s.** and is used as a burial urn to 'preserve the ashes'. We should start using it more to preserve the living corpuscles, to help 'gyrate' and move energies in the body, and to protect the cells. **Calc-s.** covers all the vascular surfaces like a '**coat**' that protects from contact with fluids, or like the egg-shell that protects yoke within the egg. If the body is deficient in **Calc-s.** the cells lack protection and '**pus**' may be the result.

Lastly, the '**Mind**' section from the proving tells us they:

- ⊙ 'sit and mediate over imaginary misfortune', '
- ⊙ grumble that his values are not understood by others',
- ⊙ have a 'hurried feeling',
- ⊙ 'despise those who do not agree with him.'
  (Here comes the sting of the scorpion's tale again!)

Calcium Sulphurica should help those born under the sign of Scorpio to be more tolerant to those around. (Not just this star sign will benefit, however, since we all need it at times when the symptoms call for it).

Remedies that follow **Calc-s.** well are **Nat. Sulph.** (which is the opposite tissue salt – see table) as well as **Kali-m.** and **Silicea,** which brings us to the next remedy.

SAGITTARIUS – the Archer

23rd November – 21st December
Silicea
Planet Jupiter

Sagittarius is the last of the three 'Fire' signs in the Zodiac. Above all Sagittarians are 'freedom lovers'; they love long journeys, foreign places and people, and new horizons. Their optimism is inspiring, and their generosity and enthusiasm combined with idealist and religious morals almost gives the idea that only the 'sky is the limit', which is the way the arrows of this archer shoot. The only way to wipe the smile off their face is to tie them down and restrict their movements; otherwise Sagittarians are generally very friendly and help others to get over the blues with the positive mind that they possess. If any suggestions made by them are not agreed with, however, they tend to ignore the 'opposition', especially if it does not serve their personal aims.

Sagittarius is opposite **Gemini** and is associated with the vibration of **TEN**, the number expressing equilibrium, willpower and supremacy. **Sagittarius** stems from the word **'Sagitta'**, meaning arrow, swift, sharp and aimed at the mark. This is analogue to the 'higher mind' and how it should progress. The symbol is the **CENTAUR**, which is half man and half horse, with bow and arrow, the arrow pointing upwards towards to the higher realms. (The word arrow is the root for arrogance!) The **CENTAUR** was viewed by the ancients as the 'savage' and the underdeveloped manifestation of the 'higher self', being only half a man and the other half animal; the untamed and vicious horse. This creature was used to symbolise the heretic and to show man divided against himself, torn between good and evil. In Greek mythology there is a story of the Thessalian centaurs who were invited to a marriage feast: One of them attempted to abduct the bride, whereupon a conflict ensued and the centaurs were driven out of the country. Thus in Christian art the Centaur was used to symbolise the passions and excesses, especially representing the sin of adultery.

The **Sagittal** stone is the **'head stone'** in an **ARCH**, also known as **'KEY STONE'**. In the body this can be compared with the FOREBRAIN, which is the last to develop and yet the first to atrophy! The cells of the forebrain are associated with intuition! When meeting people who are 'arrogant' you usually find they are extremely ignorant to spiritual matters and lacking intuition. The 'keystone' to hold up the ARCH is missing; its crown should be perfect but is not. Speaking bio-chemically, when faultless the walls will not fall down and the perfect substance here will invite clear thinking and perfect thoughts.

The **hips** and **thighs**, as well as the sciatic nerves, are physically related to Sagittarius, constituting the ARCH that supports the earthly **Torso**. If not supported by **Silicea**, both torso and mind will collapse! The word **HIP derives from HIPPO** the horse and with Sagittarius we have half man and half horse. (Plus the human brain contains a 'seahorse', the HIPPOCAMPUS, which is a long rounded elevation projecting into the lateral ventricle in the brain and is responsible for short term memory). **PEGASUS** is the winged horse with wings like an eagle and represents the balanced mind. Shakespeare knew the secret teaching when he wrote 'mount the eagle, to my palace crystalline'. This points to the next tissue salt:

Silicea, or Pure Flint

Silicea is quartz. In its crystallised form it is a rock-crystal and constitutes a large part of the Earth's crust but does not occur free in nature and therefore must be separated by chemical means. It stiffens the stems of cereal grain and is also found in animal tissue.

No matter how small the particles of Silicea, they all take the triangular form, similar to the 'Arrow' heads of the Archer. **Silicea** in Homœopathy is known as man's natural '**surgeon**', getting rid of 'pus' without a knife by pushing it to the surface.

'**Want of grit, moral and physical**' is a leading indication for **Silicea,** as without Silicea there is a '**loss of self confidence**', '**dread of failure**', and '**complaints of anticipation**' as well as '**brain fag**'. In spite of the tired brain these children are: <u>obstinate, stubborn, head-strong</u> and <u>fidgety</u>'. Their development is arrested as a result of defective nutrition from imperfect assimilation, which can be a first sign of a shortage of Silicea. The **causation** can be due to **vaccination** at an age when the body was not ready to cope with a 'triple' disease (as most vaccinations nowadays are more than just a 'single vaccine'), plus the mercury and other toxins in the vaccines that preserve them.

The homœopathic picture of **Silicea** is vast and I will just mention a few more indications here:

- ◉ They have a '**lack of vital heat**' yet display <u>sweaty feet</u>' that are <u>clammy and offensive</u>'.
- ◉ They can have '<u>profuse sweat on the head</u>', yet you will find them 'wrapping' up their head, even in humid weather, due to their sensitivity in general, but especially from their sensitivity to drafts, cold air and change of weather. Often they **do not** like to take their caps off even indoors; this is an easy way to establish if Silicea is one of the remedies required.
- ◉ Problems of **finger nails**: rough, yellow, crippled, brittle, white spots on nails.
- ◉ **Ingrown toenails.**
- ◉ **Skin: Keloids, old scars, boils and ulcers.**

As a tissue salt **Schuessler** pointed out that Silicea is an ingredient of the cells of the connective tissue, the epidermis, hair and nails. If a foreign body enters the epidermis, the skin forms pus in order to expel the invading substance and taking Silicea will speed up this job. Thus to stop ulceration and promote healing of the skin after any injury Silicea becomes the 'Surgeon's knife', as mentioned above.

CAPRICORN – the Goat

22nd December – 20th January
Calcium Phosphoricum
(Calcium Phosphate)
Planet Saturn

Once more we are looking at an 'Earth' sign with Capricorn; therefore practicality, responsibility, hard work and discipline are the orders of the day. Often we find people born under this sign being very careful with their money, sometimes to the extent of becoming a miser, like Scrooge in Charles Dickens' 'A Christmas Carol'. At the same time they have a lot of patience and can be very enduring and dutiful. They are known to be 'slow' starters in life, but make up for it by being excellent teachers to others once they have established their goals. Capricorns are very persistence individuals.

Capricorn is the 10th sign of the Zodiac and is ruled by **Saturn**, which represents the 'teacher' and builder, with order and discipline for our time on Earth. He represents the beginning; 'the Ancient of days'. **SATURN**, the Roman Deity, is identical with the Greek God **KRONOS**, meaning **'time'**, who was the son of Uranus and Gaia.

He dethroned his father as ruler of the World and was in turn dethroned by his son Zeus, or Jupiter. He devoured all his children except **Jupiter, Neptune** and **Pluto.** According to the old alchemists and astrologers **Saturn typified LEAD** and it was a very evil planet to be born under. He was the God of 'Seedtime and Harvest' and his symbol was the **scythe,** representing **OLD FATHER TIME** or the 'reaper'.

The word **January** derives from the Latin word **JANUS**, who was an ancient Italian deity. JANUS is always pictured with two faces, one of an old man and the other of a youth, looking in opposite directions, the first representing the past year, the second looking forward to the new. He was the guardian of the gates and doors. (His temple doors were thrown open at the times of war, but closed at times of PEACE).

Capricorn was at one time associated with the **UNI-Corn** (UNI for ONE and 'corn' meaning seed; the **'horn'** represents the **cerebrum**). The unicorn only exists in mythology and capturing one needed the purity of a fair maiden, thus this mythical animal became accepted as the symbol of purity and in particular of feminine chastity. On the other hand the **GOAT** that now represents Capricorn was in earlier times associated with **DEVIL** worship and the legend that the devil created the goat may well be due to this animal's destructiveness. The devil is frequently depicted as a goat, but the goat is also a symbol for **LUST**, while the sheep is the symbol of excellence and purity. The word **GO-AT** means to start something and to take the 'initiative'! However, with Janus being 'two-faced', which way do we go? Let us see if the tissue salt has the answer to this question:

Calcium Phosphate – long lasting 'Living Limestone'
or Phosphate of Lime

Calc-p. is very much needed for the **'framework'** of the body, the skeleton. As Saturn represents the 'beginning', so does our skeleton; without the framework of the bones the body would not have any foundation! It is like the oldest part of the building and is also the one that remains longest in the grave. Calc-p. is needed for the mortar (or Mucus), as no cell can be formed without it (75% of the bones are comprised of Calc-p.). **Calcium** comes from the **Latin** word **'calx'** meaning **end or goal** and **attainment.** The temple of GOD (the body) is built with **Calc Phos.**, which is the 'Living Lime-stone'. This is analogous to construction of the great pyramid of Giza; both are a perfect testimony to this long-lasting material!

Schuessler adopted Calc-p. as his leading 'anti-psoric' remedy, this also provides the indication for the Base Chakra and 'structure' to the systems. When thinking of 'psoric' and Calc-p., we have all sorts of 'under-functioning', including:

- **A delayed closure of fontanelles.**
- **A slow development of teeth in children.**
- **Later on, curvature of spine.**
- **Children, who grow tall** and **lanky.**
- **Children, who look very delicate** and **have 'growing' pains (Para-thyroid needs to be balanced).**
- **'Violent backache',** which is worse **during menses.**

Talking about the thyroid, goitre is a lack of iodine (which is an irritant, like hydrochloric acid), but also a lack of Calcium Phosphate. **Calc-p.** is very much needed in the digestive system to help assimilate food, thus we get problems due to 'faulty nutrition'. This can be a problem for the elderly, with **osteoporosis** or **osteomyelitis**, and a lack of fusion and healing in broken bones. Weak bones also break more easily. If there is a lack of **Calc-p.** in the body then mucus will collect on the tonsils and adenoids. This inflammation can be treated successfully with the tissue salt Calc-p., in combination with Silicea, without a need for the 'surgeon's knife'! (Even if the mucus has gone to the lungs, giving rise to TB, taking this salt for ten months will restore 'balance', according to clinical experience.)

The '**Mind**' **section** is vast from the extensive proving this remedy had. It is far too large to mention everything here, but the '**involuntary sighing**' is worth noting as this is easy to be observed. Furthermore:

- **The patient wishes to go to 'some other place', wanting to go away from home, yet having done so only wishing to return home, or go somewhere else.**
- **They are hard to please and have mental anxiety with all troubles.**
- **Mental strain causes headaches, especially in school children.** (A combination of **Calc-p.** + **Kali-p.** + **Nat-p.** can help during examination times; to be given **3 x daily**, starting about 3-5 days before and carry on during.)

The organs allocated to the sign of Sagittarius are the hips, thighs and sciatic nerves. When looking at the skeletal frame the **hip bones** provide a pan or cradle for the intestines. At the opposite end we have an upside-down cradle for the brain, the 'brain-pan' if you like. These pans need to be strong otherwise **PANIC**, a sudden groundless fear, will occur and if the base chakra is not working well people will suffer from 'panic-attacks'. ('Panic' has its root in the word pan).

PAN is the Greek word meaning 'ALL' or 'everything' and thus we now have the word PANACEA for 'cure all'. In mythology **Panacea** was the god of pastures and herds, yet as a deity he was represented with the upper part of a man and the body and legs of a goat, with little horns on his head (the medieval Devil was based on him). The story goes that his mother deserted him at birth and he was raised by nymphs and ended up with a very 'lustful nature'. Now, **Calc-p.** is very much found in semen and in the blood, both of which help to produce a healthy next generation and neither of which should be wasted, which could create a 'lack of' this salt.

Mineral salts, you will remember, are also termed '**Ashes**' and we have to make sure these mineral salts are not deficient in order to avoid the '**brain-pan**' **to become our** '**funeral-urn**'!

AQUARIUS – the Water-bearer

21st January – 20th February
Natrum Muriaticum – Sodium Chloride
(Common called 'Rock Salt')
Planet Saturn/Uranus

The 11th sign of the Zodiac is Aquarius and the last of the three 'Air' signs. Being an air sign they can be very creative individuals with a brilliant inspiration almost to the point of 'crankiness'. Life is never dull with Aquarians around. They can be unpredictable and unconventional; they love group activities and make good team leaders, but are restless at times, and fanatical about their ideas. The need for freedom is high on the agenda for people born under this sign of the 'new age' and at times they can be summed up in one word: Idealists. **Aquarius** is the sign of the **'Son of Man'**, the heavenly man. The opposite sign is **LEO**, the beast (remember the only beast in the Zodiac).

Uranus is the Aquarian ruler, <u>liberating changes</u>, however Saturn is the co-ruler and thus we will look at both of them. **Uranus** also means CHANGE. In Hebrew the root work '**Ur**' means **light** and Saturn rules at night while Uranus rules the day or spiritual nature.

In Greek mythology **Uranus** personifies HEAVEN. He is the son and husband of **GAIA** (Mother Earth) and the father of the **Titans** and the Cyclops (twelve by number, six male and six female, depending on the writer). However, in Genesis it states: 'there were giants on the Earth in those days'. ('Cyclops' the Greek word for 'round eye' were a group of giants that had just one eye in the centre of the forehead. Did they refer to the 3rd eye?)

The Planet **Uranus**, discovered in 1781 by Sir William Herschel (1738-1822), has fifteen known satellites; most of these were only discovered by Voyager 2 in 1986, yet some of the larger ones were known about earlier and were given names from Shakespearean plays. **Uranus** takes 84 years to 'return' through the sun signs (a complete cycle) while **Saturn** takes **28!**

Aquarius, the Latin word for 'water carrier', holds the URN which Saturn (the co-ruler) is pouring. The water is giving life upon the Earth, as without water we could not exist. As the body is over 60% water/fluids, Aquarius is physiologically and anatomically speaking the '**Saline Fluid'** of the blood (like sea water). **The corpuscles are the fish in the 'human sea'!** Only the **lower legs** and the **circulation** are assigned to this sign and therefore blood, as well as the ankles, is part of the picture of Aquarius and the remedy picture Natrum Muriaticum reflects this with '<u>weak ankles always turn under easily</u>'. Let us have a closer look at this tissue salt:

Natrum Muriaticum – our SALINE fluid, the 'sea within'.

In homœopathy the mineral Sodium Chloride, our common salt, is named **Natrum Muriaticum.** This salt absorbs water and circulates, distributing the fluids in the human organism (via osmosis). As much as we need this salt in every cell and in the blood, too much of it causes oedema ('water retention') as salt naturally attracts water. If, on the other hand, this salt if deficient in the cerebrum the corpuscles (like fish in the sea) will die, and with it '<u>reasoning</u>' dies too. When considering **fish** we should remember that the 14th letter of the Kabbalah (Hebrew, meaning to 'receive and accept oral tradition') is **N** for **NUN** (the Son), while **M** stands for **SEA** (Mother, as mentioned earlier). Thus the fish are in the internal sea of the body fluids. Without **Nat-m.** the body fluids will be inert and useless! **Nat-m.** is a **vitalised** (electrical) **salt** and a natural catalyst. One indication for deficiency would be 'tired in the morning', especially on rainy days, which may be part of the SAD syndrome (Pineal Gland should be considered here, too).

Alcohol is a toxin to the body and causes the brain to 'dry up'. Dehydration and insomnia is the result, plus the feet and legs get swollen. **Gluttony** is the first **obstacle** to overcome before entering the **'Kingdom of Heaven'**, and alcohol is part of gluttony as it is classed as an addiction; there will be no harmony to become healthy and clear headed when alcohol is known to destroy the brain cells!. When drinking alcohol we often crave 'salty' foods such as crisps or salted peanuts, which merely adds to the problem.

Dr Schuessler adopted this remedy from Homœopathy, just using a much lower potency than the 'regular 30c'. When looking at the length of symptoms this remedy calls for, one can see why we have to give it as often as we do. Symptoms include:

- ⊙ **Anaemia and brain-fag.**
- ⊙ **Lots of headaches.**
- ⊙ **Constipation** (a 'classic' here, as too much salt stops the 'natural flow').
- ⊙ **Diabetes, often craving salty food, rather than sugar.**
- ⊙ **Heart disorders, from grief, with or without depression.**
- ⊙ **Cannot even cry.**

The list is endless. These are very sensitive people who react badly to:

- ⊙ **too much Sun,**
- ⊙ **the Moon,**
- ⊙ **the seashore,**
- ⊙ **too much noise,**

Even company distresses them, etc. etc. Emotionally they are irritable and similar to salt holding on to water they hold **'grudges'** and resentment for past offences with **'fear of being rejected and hurt again'**. We know it very much as our big **'grief'** remedy, yet they cannot cry in front of others and prefer to be alone in the room and lock the door!

Candelmas was an ancient festival annually celebrated on 2nd February, right in the middle of Aquarius. In the Greek Church it is called **'Meeting the Lord'**; while in the Western church it was one of the most ancient days, honouring the Virgin Mary on 14th February. This is now St. Valentine's day, a day for the 'heart' and for LOVE. Let us take the 'grief' away and bring happiness to the body and fan the fire with Nat-m. Remember that this is an 'air' sign, but since fire cannot exist without air this will rekindle the fire. This represents 'spirit', and once we have truly found the spirit within no sadness can dwell in its place.

Genesis 1:2-3 says: 'And the Spirit of God moved upon the face of waters', and 'God said: "let there be light and there was light". To know the light is to know everything there is to know in this hemisphere. God gave us a candle to see (our brain is like the wax of a candle), but are we the right guardians of our temples to keep the light burning, or are we 'foolish' and go to sleep? 'When we were mentally blind, we thought we were happy'! Another saying is 'fools rush in where angels fear to tread', meaning that those who are unintelligent and thoughtless become involved in matters where those with wisdom and understanding think twice.

Jesus said: "You are the salt of the earth, but if the salt has lost its flavour, how will it be made salty again. It is good for nothing anymore, except to be thrown out and tramped underfoot by men!" Too much salt turns the body fluids into an acid state, but acidity, one of the biggest problems of modern man, burns away the interior and burns and burns until suffering 'burn-out', one has to leave this body as it does not serve its purpose anymore. To save our souls we must also learn to love and respect ourselves and Nat-m. will assist us to find peace within, followed by harmony, wisdom and truth.

PISCES – the Fishes

21ˢᵗ February – 20ᵗʰ March
Ferrum Phosphoricum
Planet Jupiter/Neptune

Pisces is the last sign of the **Zodiac** and is in the 12th house. It is the last of the **'Water'** signs, the others being Scorpio and Cancer. The opposite sign of Pisces is Virgo. This water sign is easily moved to tears when hearing sad stories, as they are very compassionate about other people with lots of empathy. They no not like to hear about anyone suffering, they hate injustice, and are very nostalgic and altruistic. Pisceans can be a little naïve when it come to business deals and can easily be taken for a 'ride' as they cannot believe that someone might want to cheat them. Being two fishes swimming in opposite directions, people born under this sign sometimes get restless and are not too sure which way to head, displaying 'dreaminess' about future plans. However, if in touch with the higher self the intuition is there and can foster their creativity and artistic side, as well as psychic abilities. The word Pisces is Latin for 'fish'. The true Piscean is gentle, **kind**, and 'Christ-like' in thought and deed! (The word 'kind' in German means child, to be innocent!) The two fish represent male and female and are connected by a cord symbolising that they must not be separated and must be one! The twelfth period of the cycle of life, the Zodiac, is the final stage of evolution according to the star signs when the level of Buddha, the Buddhic plane, or 'Christ-Soul' (like 'Jesus the Fish'), should be reached.

The **Ruler** of Pisces is **Neptune**, the **REVEALER** of all, expressed in visions and dreams. **Neptune**, the Roman god of the sea, is identical with Poseidon (Son of Saturn) of Greek mythology. He is represented as an elderly bearded man, carrying a trident and riding on a 'Hippocampus'; Hippo the horse and 'Kampos' meaning 'Sea Monster' (half fish/half horse). As you will realise we have met the Hippocampus before – in the brain!

Neptune is the most remote **planet** of our Solar System, taking 14 years to go through each sign of the Zodiac, thus altogether **168 years** to 'return' (twice as long as Uranus – 84 years – found under Nat-m.). Neptune is the spiritual ruler of the depth of both the Ocean and Earth. **Neptune rules both fresh** and **salt water** and it is said if the waters become foul 'monsters' will breed in it. Sea monsters are the enemy of the gods, as they are known to be lustful!

Let us briefly explore the month of **March** here, as two-thirds of Pisces is in March: **MARGO** is the Latin word meaning 'boundary', confined border, limit or extremities. When thinking of extremities the legs and feet spring to mind. 'Feet', you will remember, are the only body parts left for the Piscean. With these feet you can of course 'march' or 'set off' into the future, or to a 'new school', i.e. the school of life!

Pisces provides **'the fountain of life'** in renewed and strong blood. The iron will give a strong shield to the aura and the phosphor will let us 'sparkle'. I am sure you will agree, we cannot ask for much more from this vital tissue salt. 'For the life of the flesh is in the blood, for it is the blood that marketh atonement for the soul', Lev.17:11. (**At-one-ment** for the **Soul!**) Disease and lack of at-one-ment or deficiency (sin) is the cause of death.

Astrologically the **feet** belong to **Pisces**; if not standing on your own feet it means 'you never grow up'. I also found that 'STRESS' is mentioned under this sign and in modern society we have plenty of that! Let us therefore investigate how **Ferrum Phosphoricum** can help us to overcome stress and to stand on our own feet.

Ferrum Phosphoricum – the 'FOUNTAIN OF LIFE'
Also known as **Phosphate of Iron**

Schuessler used Ferr-phos. as a great therapeutic remedy in cases of :
- ⊙ 'first stages of febrile conditions',
- ⊙ for all kinds of **inflammatory disorders**
- ⊙ for **anaemia,**
- ⊙ as well as using it for **'taking colds easily'!**

However, before studying the remedy picture of Ferr-phos., let us look at a few references to detect the meaning of iron: We already know that 'Phosphor' is the 'bearer of light', what does 'Iron' symbolise?

Iron in Hebrew is **'piety'**, which also means 'holiness, true godliness'! **Ferrum** is the Latin for **iron** and is derived from the word **'fero'**, meaning to bear, to bring, to carry, which is the true nature of this **'magnetic salt'**; the magnet attracts, 'attracting life'. Iron gives strength to the body; think of steel, which is made from iron. **Iron** is one of the most important metals in nature and can be found in the atmosphere – meteoric iron – especially in the higher strata, which are filled with invisible specks or atoms of **Ferrum**. Therefore, the watery ether above is filled with the smallest particles of iron, which is the same as the iron in the Earth and in man's body.

Lack of iron causes **desperation** and **discouragement**. The **blood** becomes 'lifeless' and the air outside the body 'is heavy on the chest' as oxygen is lacking, too. Iron carries oxygen in the arterial system and therefore a depletion of iron results in a reduction of oxygen content in the blood, leading to **'stagnation and putrefaction'; the 'inner' sea 'dies' slowly,**. (This is one of the reasons why CANCER can develop!)

The venous system, too, is affected with 'congestion' and thus a leading feature for this tissue salt, apart from anaemia and haemorrhages, there are disorders of the veins with great **physical** and **mental lassitude, prostration** and **nervousness.**

Schuessler gave the following explanation: "Iron and its salts possess the property of attracting oxygen. The iron contained in the blood corpuscles takes up the inhaled oxygen, thereby supplying with it all the tissues of the organism. The sulphur contained in the blood corpuscles and in other cells in the form of sulphate of potash (Kali Sulph.) assists in transferring oxygen to all the cells containing iron and the sulphate of potash." Usually potassium will be deficient as well as iron, and both are very much needed in the Solar Plexus as one is the metal here and the other an important mineral. If the sea of our body fluids and blood corpuscles are depleted of iron, youth and vitality, the 'spark of life', will leave. We are no longer a **'magnet'** to others.

The **'Mind'** section bears this out with:
- ⊙ **'fear of going into a crowd',**
- ⊙ **'indifference to pleasurable things',**
- ⊙ **'aversion to company'**
- ⊙ **'keeping quiet'.** (Not exactly the person everyone wants to talk to!)

On the other side of the same coin we have **'very talkative, hilarious and excited'.**

From my own experience they often repeat themselves, which can get very boring to the listener in the long run. Subsequently this type is not a 'crowd puller' either.

People lacking this salt can get:

- ⊚ '**easily flushed**', yet due to '**anaemia**' are generally very pale, with night sweating.
- ⊚ lack of iron in females often presents itself with 'menses every week' or there about (too frequent and too much loss of blood).
- ⊚ In **children** we have '**nose-bleeding**', as well as '**bed-wetting**',
- ⊚ often suffering from tonsillitis or acute otitis.

At the first signs of these symptoms give Ferr-phos. several times daily. To avoid operations on the ear, nose or throat this remedy needs to be given for months to build up strength and resistance.

One final point to consider here: If you have a fever (or cold) it means that the body is doing a 'house cleaning'. Take Ferr. Phos. at the first sign, combined with **Kali-m.** to get rid of 'pus'. Follow with **Calc Phos**, as phlegm points to Calcium deficiency and it stimulates the Pituitary Gland. Restoring the 'fountain of life' with Ferr-p. will put the colour back into the skin, not only giving a healthy and attractive look, even without any make-up, but appearing naturally 'fit for life'!

Conclusion

The last and final part has to be the POTENCY!

One question that is always on the agenda is potency. As Homœopaths we are forever wondering whether or not we are 'matching the right' potency to the symptom of the case? On this subject we can get as many answers as we have questions. Our intuition often provides the right response, but as yet no hard rules are supplied and I am not in a position to give all the answers of what is missing here myself. All the same I would like to put forward some suggestions. Having explained the chakras and the subtle bodies I hope that my understanding of them can provide some answers to potencies, which I would like to share here:

For the physical body I suggest giving the potency of 30c or lower, especially when wanting to support the organs. For example, with the tissue salts or other organ drainage etc, there is a great variety to choose from, with potencies of a 3x to a 30c. This might also be for an acute symptom, where we look for the name of the disease and choose accordingly, like an acute tonsillitis that might call for Belladonna 30c, or a cramp could be relieved with Mag. Phos.30c

From the **Physical body** to the **Emotional body** anything from **30c to 200c** is appropriate as this is energising the auric field, which is about 30cm around the body, and removes blockages. Here the feelings can be expressed by the patient, such as **feeling** 'hot/cold/tired/not thirsty/always exhausted, or weakness from mental strain, lack of sleep, too much work, feeling sore all over, bruised or numbness in limbs' etc.

For the Mental body we can choose from the **200c to a 1M**. As our remedies are generally on this scale (with 1M being the potency that immediately follows 200c) we might not want to deviate, but there is nothing to stop us from using intermediate potencies, for example a 300c or 400c, etc. (especially if you like using machine-made remedies and are good at dowsing for the right potency for the patient). Into this category I would place **emotions** like: **'sad', 'angry', 'humiliated'** and **'indifferent'** etc., as the **'drama of life'** is taking place on this level.

For the **Astral body** potencies **between 1M and 10M** are a good choice, again with scope to choose any intermediate potency within this range. The 'delusion of being followed' or 'hearing voices' would be a very good reason to go this high as this of course could be an 'entity' being attached, as discuss earlier (although not necessarily and could well be only a delusion).

Feeling 'criticised by everyone' could certainly be placed here, as well as feeling 'abandoned by friends' and 'nobody loves me'! Well known to Homœopaths for instance, are the 'delusions' of patients needing Platina or Sulphur who believe that 'he/she is a great person'; the way that the patient dresses could easily confirm this. Either they will be 'overdressed for the occasion' and considering themselves quite noble, or they are dressed very scruffily, not being bothered about what they wear and yet boasting about how 'great they are'. Taking everything into account could call for a 10M to make a real difference in changing their attitude.

After the **Astral body** we reach the **Etheric body** with **10M to 50M potencies**. Being connected to a past life we have to assess the family background. This helps us to see which miasms we chose in this life to see what lessons we might want to learn and come to terms with. This miasmatic connection could be expressed by the behaviour of the patient in daily life, as well as during the consultation, such as if a patient starts to cry instead of just saying 'I am sad about this or that'. Another example is of a patient who is not just *feeling* in a hurry, but who is also sitting at the edge of their seat, hardly taking their coat off, and being agitated and talking with great speed. Apart from the right remedy the potency should match this 'urgency' about everything.

The **Buddhic body** is not one we would treat 'on a daily basis' as we are reaching up from a **50M to a CM**. Here we want to make changes in our life and to leave the old behind, making a fresh start. This high potency might give the courage to do so.

The **Causal body** could be reached with a **MM potency**, which once more is not something we need to choose regularly. However, that is not to say that in years to come we might not want to use those higher potencies more often, as people need finer 'tuning' as a result of the raising of the energy levels.

Nothing is written is stone and I very much hope that I am offering an additional 'guideline' that can further be worked on, rather than providing a perfect 'recipe'.

Earlier in the book I also mentioned that I would present the Lord's Prayer as a tool to strengthen and protect our energy fields. This is in no way a suggestion that it is the 'only tool', but it is the best known to me as a Christian. However, that is not to say that Christianity has all the answers; my search for spirituality became a quest that has led me away from the main church that could not provide me with the teaching I was looking for. I could no longer accept what the church had cleverly 'forgotten' to teach over the last 1500 years or so. There was a time when the teaching of re-incarnation in Christianity was not for the 'crazy' new-age people, as it is still so often looked upon these days. In former times it was common knowledge and anyone having studied early Christian theology must be aware of it. Why the church has not been able to change and admit their 'shortcomings' on the subject of 'life after death' remains a mystery, at least to me anyway. That there is 'a life' after death is a reality that we all have to confront. We all have to die and we cannot change this fact, and therefore we are faced with the question: What 'kind of life' is out there and how will it be to have no physical body?

I was exceptionally lucky to have had a father who followed and instructed me and my siblings from an early age in the teachings of Rudolf Steiner (1861-1925), the German Philosopher who started the movement of Anthroposophy in 1909, which now has its own recognised 'energy' medicines (Anthroposophical medicines). Steiner very much believed that colour therapy would be part of the medicine for the 21st century! Now, as Homœopaths, we too work much more with colour remedies, which we can relate to the chakras, or use them for their own merits.

Steiner was the founder of the famous Waldorf School in which 'body, spirit and soul' are very much taken into consideration when teaching the young. I was not fortunate enough to attend one of these schools as there were not many in existence when I was a child. However, I recognise the excellent education they offer, as my father would instruct us in some of their philosophies. Consequently, being familiar with the whole concept of the 'other side', the unseen, I had to find out for myself. Eagerly I read every book I could find on the subject from a very early age and could never understand why people could not share my enthusiasm to talk about these things, until I finally realised it is the 'fear of death'. (Fear, remember is seated in the base chakra, being 'stuck'!)

Most people are so fearful they never even want to think about dying and getting their house in order beforehand. They brush away the subject as if it will never happen to them! It might happen to everybody else but somehow not to them; they are going to be spared! Personally I cannot see any comfort in that! How much more comforting is it if you can believe and understand that there is no end and that the soul just leaves the body, but still has 'a-life' (in spirit). It means that the soul does not have to wait for the 'final judgement day'; it will judge itself then and there and review the life, only to learn from its mistakes and then move on to the next life and lesson. The soul will understand immediately all the pain it has ever given or 'created' in others by its personal 'wrong actions and exploits', as it will have to go through 'suffering' the pain, upsets and emotions it has caused. Depending on the life just left behind I am sure that this could be 'hell' for a lot of people and maybe that is what the scriptures talked about when mentioning such a dreadful place in the 'afterlife'.

Nowadays there are numerous books of 'near-death' experiences and we should all familiarise ourselves with these tales of a person who has 'died' during an operation, only to be revived by doctors and their modern instrumentation. Most likely the person will narrate their experience of being 'dead' as indescribably beautiful; they loved the feeling of liberty and freedom without being restricted within the 'shell' of the body, felt greatly at peace, and mostly did not really wish to return to their physical body. To me this indicates that this is certainly not a place that one needs to be fearful of! If one chooses **not** to return to the body then 'helpers' are at hand to assist the <u>passage over the threshold</u>, so to speak.

These more recently written books in modern everyday language are much easier to read than those of Rudolf Steiner, for example, who wrote a vast amount of books on this very subject; too many, in fact, for anyone to read. For anyone still sceptical on the subject I recommend they read some of the books by Dolores Cannon who 're-discovers' former lives of her clients through hypnotic regression. Such books enhance all of our understanding of the human history, of our planet Earth and why we have come to this planet and what we are collectively trying to achieve.

As mentioned earlier I was in the fortunate position to start on the subject of what is now called spirituality at a young age. This, by the way, was one of the reasons I became a Homœopath in the first place, since it was the only medicine that made sense to me! I could identify with the potencies and understood what they were trying to achieve on a deeper level. Going to college and studying was just as if I needed to be retold something I had already learned, but somehow forgotten again. I only needed to be reminded and it all made sense and came back to life. In other lifetimes I am sure I have 'practised' healing, either with herbs or crystals or whatever was 'taught' at the time. And I hope that it was always in a 'gentle' way, like we now have in the 'healing art of Homœopathy'.

Coming back to the prayer, the Lord's Prayer, which should be said on a daily basis in order to 'cleanse' and strengthen the aura. We start with: *'Our Father, who art in heaven, hallowed be Thy Name'*, with which we address and honour the **Causal body**.

Going down to the **Buddhic** level we acknowledge that: *'Thy kingdom come, Thy will be done'!*

While on the **Etheric** level we agree that it is: *'on earth, as it is in heaven'.*

On the **Astral** level we ask: *'Give us today our daily bread'*, as surely we need this source of energy to be fed every day, like recharging the battery, making sure we are strong and do not have holes in the aura to creating easy access for 'spirits' to be able to attach themselves.

And on the **Mental** level we pray: *'and forgive us our trespasses, as we forgive those who trespass against us'*, as we need the right mental attitude to be able to do so.

The **Emotional body**, you will remember, is one of the most difficult to overcome and here we beg: *'and lead us not into temptation'!* Temptations are everywhere, all the time! You only need to go into a shop and see the temptations on offer. We must decide if and what we need, and be in command and not be like 'lemmings all jumping off the cliff'. 'Retail-therapy', as it is called these days, is not a therapy for the soul; it feeds the emotions as we are 'happy' to have treated ourselves! But how long does this happiness last? This was just one simple example and there are lots more, especially when it comes to choosing partners and the 'emotions' that come with these choices. No condemnation here on my behalf, just statements of how we have to be on 'guard' when we ask for help with the 'temptations'.

On the last body, the **Physical body**, we request: *'deliver us from evil'*, as 'evil' (hurting others) is so easily done on this level.

The rest: *'for Thine is the kingdom, and the power and the glory,* for *ever and ever'.* **Amen.** We just give credence to the 'Al-mighty' that without the belief in our higher self, as well as the omnipresence of all that is and ever will be, we would never be here in the first place.

May the content of this book be an inspiration for all who come into contact with it and share my passion for Homœopathy.

The Bowel Nosode Programme

~~Before giving Lyc., Calc. & Thuja use this 3-5 month~~ of 'clearing out' programme.
Start with the **Base chakra: Morgan 200 – split dose** to clear intestines, skin as well as clearing medical treatment. Followed by *Sulph. 10M* – single dose* – one week later.

- give cells salts according to the star sign of the patient to assist Sulphur to work.

....

Sacral chakra: 3 to 4 weeks later – Syc-co. 200c – split dose – to clear **VACCINATION**, if these were given and clearly cause a blockage – **followed by Merc-sol. 10M – single dose** – one week later, (as Mercury is/was one of the ingredients in the vaccines as early as the 1930s.)

Depending on the vaccine you can support it with:
- Skook, or Sil. if the vaccine caused a skin problem.
- Gels. low potency if it was the flue vaccine = NBWS.
- Kali-Chlor. one to consider as a support if the kidneys need further detoxification from Mercury.
- Kali-Chlor. if he child suffers nosebleeds.

....

Solar Plexus: 3 or 4 weeks later – Morgan-Gaertner 200c – split dose – if the patient suffers from all sorts of ALLERGIES including: FOOD, POLLEN, CHEMICALS, etc. or ANTI-BIOTICS = NBWS
Followed by **Sil. 10M or Nit-ac 10M – single dose** – one week later.

Support with low potency – twice a day:
- All-c. or Ars. low in case of hay-fever type allergies,
- Ars-i., for asthma type cases.
- Apis tendency to anaphylactic shock
- Urt-u., this includes hives.
- Phos. or Nat-c. sensitive to chemicals.
- Nat-p. or China – Antibiotics NBWS

....

Heart chakra: 3 or 4 weeks later – Proteus 200c – split dose – to clear the nervous system and to relieve any intracranial tension, followed by *Lyc. 10M – single dose* – one week later.

- support with *Kali-phos.* AM and at bedtime with *Kali Mur.* for 2-3 weeks.

....

Throat chakra: 3 or 4 weeks later – Gaertner 200c – split dose – to clear Colon/Liver/Spleen & Kidneys.
Followed by *Calc Carb. 10M – single dose* – one week later.

- support with cells salts – *Nat Sulph.* AM and *Calc Sulph.* PM for 3 weeks.

....

Third Eye or Brow chakra: 3 or 4 weeks later Dysentery Co. 200c – split dose – to clear every tissue of the body, as this is the Nosode suitable for many slow and insidious chronic states – followed by *Thuja 10M – single dose* – one week later.

- support with *Nat-phos* AM and *Sil.* PM for 2 weeks
- *Calc-f.* AM and *Kali Mur* PM for a further 2-3weeks.

....

Crown chakra: Further detoxification can follow with **Bac. No. 7 200c – split dose** – followed by either *Clay 10M* single dose, being such a good purifier – one week later, or use:

.A 10M *in England*, due to the amount of tea drunk by some people.
.lternatively **Coffea 10M** for the same reason and very much in vogue these days.
Can be supported with:

- Ars-i., Calc-i., Ferr-i., Nat-i. or Merc-i-f. helping to stimulate the metabolism.

....

If the need for **Bac. No. 10 – split dose** – arises then **Sepia or Pic-Ac. 10M** single dose a week later, can be used as the associated remedy.

- Support with cells salts, either Ferr-p. or Calc-f., twice daily.

....

* Should there be a severe aggravation to Sulph. 10M – esp. an abscess or ulcer, as well as eczema, you can be sure that the next miasmatic remedy to be considered is Syph.

THE BOWEL NOSODES TABLE

REMEDY	Morgan Bach/Pure	Sycotic Co	Morgan Gaertner	Proteus	Gaertner	Dys-co.	Bac.No.7	Bac.No.10
CENTRE & PLANETS	Base Chakra (SATURN)	Sacral (JUPITER)	Solar Plexus (MARS)	Heart (SUN)	Throat (VENUS)	Brow (MERCURY)	Brow/Base (Moon)	Crown (MOON)
REGION in the body	Skin & Circulation	Mucous & Synovial membranes	NERVES & Urinary; Gastrointestinal. Tract/ right Side	MIND, Central & peripheral nervous Syst.	Nutrition Connective Tissue	Nerves, Heart Circulation Digestion	Premature senility Elderly & debauch	
MENTAL and EMOTIONAL	Anxiety Health Introspective & Depression unstable Suicidal tendency Avoids company, but often shows mental anxiety when left alone. Fear of crowds Fears: of the World, of crisis, ill health, the unknown Tense, active, weepy & irritable	IRRITABILITY Nervous/tense tempered/cross Fear of the dark, alone, animals esp. dogs. Night mares/terrors. Twitching of facial muscles Blinking eyelids Quick temper Restless Mentally exhausted	Nervous breakdown Apprehension, fear – crowds, excitement, company, closed places. Fear of nervous breakdown Jealous. Fastidious Offended easily Quick temper Restless	Nervous tension "Brain storms" Sudden fits of rage/ anger. Aggravated by contradiction. Could commit murder if crossed. Aversion company Hysterial Destructiveness Fixed ideas stubborn Quick temper Stammering of the old Mentally exhausted	Hypersensitive to all impressions (Physical & psychical) Intelligent Overactive brain under-nourished body. Desires company Nervous Excitable HYPERACTIVE Resentment	Nervous tension ANTICIPATION Full of fears. Fear in lifts. On the train/bus Storms & thunder Of the dark, closed places. Claustrophobic Anxious over trifles, over the future, worries that unable to cope. Hypersensitive to criticism, thus fear of public appearances, Insecure – lack of confidence Always stressed and in a hurry. Easily excited & flustered. Aversion company/ strangers– yet alone agg. Memory – poor Mentally exhausted	Keynote: Phys. & mental FATIGUE Tense and tired (unfit for any mental effort, producing extreme physical exhaustion). Thinking of work agg. Prostration Thoughts of doing anything cause agg. Mentally weak Idiocy Senility	Anxious, overactive mind Irritable and depressed

The Bowel Nosodes Table

REMEDY	Morgan Bach/Pure	Sycotic Co	Morgan Gaertner	Proteus	Gaertner	Dys-co.	Bac.No.7	Bac.No.10
PHYSICAL	CONGESTION in Menopause = hot flushes. Congestive Headaches = frontal, vertex & occipital Post-nasal catarrh. Rheumatism, esp. neck & shoulder LIVER = Gallstones ACIDITY - food amel. Varicose veins. (Scirr.) Phlebitis. Tonsillitis recurrent (PSOR)	Restless feet in bed at night Weekly headache (left sided) <noise, before or after menses > heat, rest Lumbar-sacral pain & stiff all over Anal and rectal prolapse Conjunctivitis. Eyes: opacity vitreous Torticollis Tonsillitis: recurrent	Constipation (more common than looseness) Renal colic/stones Sinusitis (frontal & maxillaries) Nasal catarrh & post nasal secretion. Eyes: Opacity vitreous Tonsillitis: recurrent) (TUB, Syph)	Keynote: Suddenness & violence ACIDITY, heartburn. Palpitation after excitement. Diarrhoea from excitement. Digestive allergies Empty sensation in stomach not > eating Migraines. Pressing frontal headache <one weeks before menses <morning Lots of Vertigo	Marked emaciation. Digestive problems start in childhood, vomits everything. Acidosis attacks Headache & vomiting, diarrhoea every few weeks. Sweets agg. Constipation & Diarrhoea offensive	Tension felt in stomach & heart area Palpitations & heartburns. <before events Violent headache & diarrhoea 5/6 motions day Disposition to indigestion & loose stool. (Has been going on for year). Frontal, blinding headache, over eyes. or in vertex, regularly every 7 – 14 days Tonsillitis: recurrent (carc.) Sudden shocks on falling asleep.	Fibrous rheumatism, <neck and back. Stiffness neck = 'cracks like a nut' Osteoporosis Rheumatism of wrist. Osteo-arthritis knees. Feet painful, gout in toes. Poor muscle tone, limbs stiff. Stabbing pain – hips Catarrhal deafness Retinal thrombosis Asthma < 2 AM	Bowel motion first thing in the morning or Bowel motion sluggish Tenderness coccyx Asthma Cough <morning Offensive breath Spongy gums Nasal catarrh Pain in Gallbladder. Pain – left & right iliac fossa

THE BOWEL NOSODES TABLE

REMEDY	Morgan Bach/Pure	Sycotic Co	Morgan Gaertner	Proteus	Gaertner	Dys-co.	Bac.No.7	Bac.No.10
GENERAL	Blood pressure HIGH (cheeks red) DRYNESS mucous membrane & Skin + burning (cracks, scaly, red raw & weeping) CONGESTION = cutaneous, pulmonary, hepatic, intestinal & cerebral Goitre - Thyroid Duodenum: Ulcers Stomach: peptic ulcers Water-brash, Heart-burn, belching Gallstones & Gallbladder problems. Vertigo: esp. with high Blood-pressure Meniere's disease Smell – lost Enuresis Night-terrors	SYCOSIS Catarrhal conditions (nose, throat, bronchi, gastro-intestinal, & urogenitals) HAYFEVER Chronic cystitis FOOD ALLERGIES Goitre - Thyroid Acidosis (Nat-p + Mag-c.) Vomiting: Nocturnal, stomach must empty Smell lost Nightmares, Night-terrors Dreams of dead people	FLATULENT DISTENSION Allergies & Dermatitis Cancer in general (CARC., Med, Scirr., Psor. Syph. + x-ray) Stomach: Ulcers Duodenum: ulcers Enuresis	Circulatory disorders Angina Pectoris SPASM (Raynaud's Syndrome) Meniere's Disease Intermittent Claudi-fication CRAMPS: legs, calf, icy cold feet, Epilepsy Ailments during or since convalescence Heartburns Vertigo	Keynote: Malnutrition Coeliac disease (proper nutrition prevented by sensitivity to Gluten – G. are the nitrogenous part of wheat & other grains) Ketosis Vomiting: Headache with Sweets: agg. Acidosis	Appetite as a rule is poor in the morning. <eating thirst & desire for cold drinks, but stomach worse afterwards Physical restlessness Hay fever Palpitations Tachycardia Extra Systoles Goitre – Thyroid Thyroid – toxic Stomach: Ulcers, Dilation and distension, Splashing in. Heartburns + belching Duodenum: ulcers Vertigo: <excitement agg. after sleep Dreams of: Burglars/ fire/ Dead people Falling from height	Blood pressure Low + slow pulse Relaxed fibrous tissue with tendency to the formation of rheumatic nodules. Light sleeper. Loss of sexual func-tions. Syncope: (Brief faint-ing fits) Stomach: Distension, Fullness <after eating	Averse to breakfast

145

The Bowel Nosodes Table

REMEDY	Morgan Bach/Pure	Sycotic Co	Morgan Gaertner	Proteus	Gaertner	Dys-co.	Bac.No.7	Bac.No.10
FEMALE	Dermatitis on breast. Eczema, scaly on Genitals. Fibroids Uterus. Polyps Uterus (Thyr., Carc., med., tub.). Bartholinitis (glands at vagina inflamed). Ovaries painful. Hot Flushes – due to congestion at menopause. Cystitis	Amenorrhoea (Thyr) / *Dysmenorrhoea.* Genital warts, herpes & uterine polyps. Ovarian Cysts. Fallopian tubes inflamed. Ovaries painful < left, < during menses. Inflammation Vagina. Gonorrhoea. Hair on face, upper lip. Cystitis (Mutabile) (Chlamydia or E-Coli, Med.).	*Dysmenorrhoea.* PMT. Warts on NIPPLES. Leucorrhoea = thick, brown, corrosive & offensive. *Cystitis*	Inflammation vagina – brown discharge + discharge between menses (Foll.). Boils in vagina. Recent Gonorrhoea. Burning pains in urethra		Dysmenorrhoea. Hot flushes at Menopause with excitement. Urging to urinate when travelling	Sexual weakness. Vulva pains.	Cracks Genitalia
MALE	Eruptions – Scrotum, Vesicular	Herpes Groin		Recent Gonorrhoea. Burning pains in urethra			Impotence. Feeble flow of urine	Genital – dry. Genitals – raw
CHILDREN	Mongoloid. History of repeated nasal congestion & lung. Catarrhal deafness. Bronchitis each Winter. Growing pains in legs (Para-Thyr.). Nail-biting. Eczema: Infantile. Umbilicus: moist. Worms (Scirr.) parasites	Ailments from vaccination. Anorexia. Asthma, Hay-fever. Meningitis. Bedwetting. Restless sleep. Nightmares/terrors – won't sleep alone. Perspiration (esp. on head at night). Nail-biting. Eczema: Infantile Ear-Wax: more than usual	Cough in morning & on waking. Asthma. Shouts in sleep. Nail-biting	Outburst of violent temper, throws any missile, kicks, strike. Lies on floor kicks & screams, when angry. Beats head against the bed or knocks head on things. Rectal spasm in children. Worms: Threadworms	Keynote: Malnutrition, active brain but poorly developed bodies & muscle. Restless sleep, night terror, wants to sleep besides mother. (Wants light on). Emaciation (infantile). Lack of reaction in children. Bites nails. Worms (Carc., Med, Tub.)	Hypersensitive nature. Stammering – with excitement. Blush easily. Shy. Hay-fever. Twitching of face/eyelids. Restlessness, fidgets. Desire to wander. Boys/Girls = Masturbate (Carc., med., Scirr.). Growing pains		*Anorexia*

The Bowel Nosodes Table

REMEDY	Morgan Bach/Pure	Sycotic Co	Morgan Gaertner	Proteus	Gaertner	Dys-co.	Bac.No.7	Bac.No.10
Extremities & Skin	ECZEMA (Dry cracked, fissured, itching, weepy – on chin, in ear passage Forehead *Dermatitis* Easily bruised Sensitive to SUN, + wool Acne Acne Rosacea Numbness – Arms, legs and feet Alopecia Athlete's foot Boils: in ears, on the neck and vulva Chilblains: esp. feet Cyst: Tarsal Finger joints swollen & painful *Stiffness* <morning Hands stiff + poor grip Stiffness legs, knees	Face puffy, esp. in the morning under eyes WARTS, (Med. Psor. Syph.) Warts – Genital, rectum Large, jagged or flat Dermatitis Nails brittle. Cracks on heels and fingertips. Fingers deformed = nodules on fingers. Numbness – fingers Skin – oily Blisters Alopecia Ringworm (Med.) Chilblains: Feet < for heat Cyst: tarsal & Sebaceous Stiffness: Ankles, Back, Neck. Hips.	Crippled toenails Eruptions about eye-brows (crusty) Excessive heat of feet at night Shingles (Herp-z., Vario.) Psoriasis (Thyr., Tub.) Acne Rosacea Cyst: on eyelids Styes eyelids (Tub., Psor.)	Eruptions – boils maturing slowly Awkwardness of hands, drop things Nails split. Skin: pigmented Sensitive to light Numbness – legs, feet, fingers Herpes Shingles Cracked lips Hair falls out. Boils: in vagina Chilblains Cyst: on eyelids	RESTLESS hands and feet Eruption back & neck. Soles of feet itch < night. Herpes around mouth. Blisters on Soles Chapped hand < Winter Boils: on arms, Axillae, or legs Chilblains: Hands < Winter	Restless hands Face flushes easily – puffiness of eyelids & cheeks. Trembling from excitement. Backache & Spondylitis. Rheumatism neck/ shoulder Warts: feet and hands Ringworm (BAC, TUB.,) all over the body = Psor. Cracked fingertips Blisters	Cracks on knuckles, tips of fingers. Palms nippy, scaly and hot. Blood vessels burst, in fingers Sensitive to cold, and cold/damp Stiffness: Neck, Cracks like a nut + legs – stiffness Swollen limbs	Dermatitis of skin flexes. Ringworm. Warts: hands, flat or pointed
TIME	<night <First thing in the morning	<2-3 AM or sleepless until 3 AM	<4-8 PM Drowsy after meals/ food	<morning Sudden onset		<night <2-3 AM <3-6 AM Insomnia from mental activity	Light sleep Takes 2 hours to go to sleep. Wakes 2 or 3 AM	
Modalities	<Sun, wool, <washing >continued motion	<cold, damp, weather >seaside Light agg.	>passing flatus up/down (full after eating ever so little)	>Mountains >Ascending high <Cold <Winter		>eating >presence strangers Light agg.	<cold/draught <cold damp air Excessive sweat	

THE BOWEL NOSODES TABLE

REMEDY	Morgan Bach/Pure	Sycotic Co	Morgan Gaertner	Proteus	Gaertner	Dys-co.	Bac.No.7	Bac.No.10
FOOD	Crave: Fats, sweets, eggs, butter <rich food, eggs	Aversion: Eggs, fat, milk & milk pudding, cream, salt, vegetables and tomatoes, potatoes, tea, vinegar <eggs <fat, <onions, oranges Appetite diminished. Aversion breakfast Fastidious and picky	Craves: Sweets, salt, hot spicy food Aversion: Butter eggs	Aversion: raw food/salads Garlic & onions <chocolate <eggs	Desire: Cheese, eggs, milk/pudding, sweets/sugar Aversion: Bread, butter, meat, fish .	Desires: Fats & rich food, milk, salt, sugar, sweets	Aversion to fat, tomatoes Appetite diminished Aversion breakfast	Aversion: eggs bread, tomatoes, tea Craves: Sweets, chocolate, fried fish
Associated Remedies	SULPH. CALC. PSOR. + PLB. Alum., Bary-c Calc-f, Calc-p. Calc-sil., Cean. Carb-v, Carb-s. Cadm-s. Dig., Graph. Hecla-l. Lyc., Mag-c, Nat-c. Petr. Puls., Sep. Sil., Stront-c. Symph, Thios., Tub.	THUJ., Nit-ac. + Stann. Alf., Ant-t., Bac, Cann-i, Card-m., Chel. Chin., Chol. Hydr, Med., Nat-m. Nat-s, Nux-v. Podo, Puls., Rhus-t. Sep. Tarax. Tub.	LYC. + Ferr. Ferr-p. Acon., Apis, Arn., Bellis-p. Calen, Canth., Crat., Ham., Hell., Hep., Hyper., Kali-bi, Kali-c Lach. Merc-s, Nat-m, Nat-s, Nux-v., Plant, Puls, Sang., Sil., Staph., Tarax. Urt-u.	NAT-M. + AUR. Aur-m , Am-m Apis, Bary-c, Bary-m. Bor, Cact., Con., Cupr. Dig., Euph., Ferr-m., Glon., Helia. Ign., Kali-m., Mag-m, Mur-ac, Sec, Sol.,	SIL. + CUPR. CARC, PHOS Tub.+ Bac. Apis, Benz-ac. Berb., Caul. Calc-c, Calc-f. Calc-p, Calc-sil. Equis. Kali-p. Merc. Nat-p. Petro., Phyt., Puls., Sabal, Sars., Staph., Solid., Zinc-p.	ARG-N, ARS., + MERC. Anac, Ant-t., Cadm-s. Cham, Dros. Ign. Kalm. Kali-m. Lob., Lyc., Nux-v. Proteus Spon. Verbasc. Verat-alb. Verat-viv.	Arg. Brom. & Iod. in combination with Potassium Kali-i., Kali-p. Kali-brom. Anac., Ars-i. Aven. Calc-i, Cina, Cocc., Coff. Con. Gink., Hell., Hyoc., Ip, Luna, Merc-i-f. Nat-i., Nux-v., Op., Passi. Stram., Tea Valer.,	Sepia+ Pic-ac Aral. Calc-p. Kali-bi. Nat-s., Thuj.

"PLANET"	CHAKRA		STAR-SIGN
	ELEMENT	MIASM	& Tissue Salts
MOON ☾	CROWN CHAKRA The Feminine Principle – Goddess LUNA "Spiritual Awareness" INTUITION / INSTINCT UNCONCIOUS	 PSORIC	CANCER *4th House* Calc-Fluor
MERCURY ☿	THIRD EYE – BROW CHAKRA WISDOM MERCURY – The MESSENGER - DUALITY has a 'Shadow Side' COMMUNICATION / INSPIRATION 'active' Intelligence	 SYCOTIC	GEMINI *3rd House* Kali-Mur VIRGO *6th House* Kali-Sulph
VENUS ♀	THROAT CHAKRA UNITY / HARMONY / DIPLOMACY Social contacts Feelings – Knowledge of 'good & evil' ETHER	 TUBERCULAR/CANCER	TAURUS *2nd House* Nat-Sulph LIBRA *7th House* Nat-Phos
SUN ☉	HEART CHAKRA The Masculine Principle - The WILL - The Father (to be at one - atonement - with divine spirit) LOVE / LIFE / VITALITY AIR	 SYPHILITIC	LEO *5th House* *The Place of rebirth* Mag-Phos
MARS ♂	SOLAR PLEXUS FIRE / PASSION / WAR to 'conquer' the World FIRE	 TUBERCULAR/CANCER	ARIES *1st House* Kali-Phos SCORPIO *8th House* Calc-Sulph
JUPITER ♃	SACRAL CHAKRA EXPANSION & MOVEMENT – wants to make the World a better place WATER	 SYCOTIC	SAGITTARIUS *9th House* Silicea PISCES *12th House* Ferr-Phos
SATURN ♄	ROOT CHAKRA The 'LAUNCH-PAD' SECURITY / PARENTS / HOME + NATION IDENTITY – Lack of – resulting in FEAR EARTH	 PSORIC	AQUARIUS *10th House* Nat-Mur CAPRICORN *11th House* Calc-Phos

BOWEL NOSODES, CHAKRAS & Related Remedies

BOWEL NOSODE (Sarcodes)	CHAKRAS / Organ/Gland / "Keyword"	Related Remedies
EXHAUSTION **BAC No. 10** **BAC No. 7** (Pituitary Gland)	CROWN / PITUITARY Gland / "Physical & Mental Fatigue"	Arg., Ars-i., **BROM.**, Iod. (in combination with other remedies: Calc-i., Ferr-i., Kali-i., Merc-i-f., Nat-i.), Lac-c., Lyss., Pic-ac. Hyos. / Carc., Cand-a. / **LOTUS**, Cotton, Luna, Moonstone, Rainbow, *Purple*
NERVES **DYS-CO.** (Pineal Gland)	BROW (THIRD EYE) / PINEAL Gland / "Anticipation"	Anac., **ARG-N.**, **ARS.**, Cadm-s., Kali-p., Kalm., Lyc., Merc., Nux-v.., Tarent., Verat-a.,-v. / Bac., **CAND-A.**, Prot., Tub-b./,-k. / **LOTUS**, Amethyst, Ash, Goldfish, Hornbeam, *Indigo*, Ruby, Salix Fragilis, Stonehenge
CHILDREN'S NOSODE **GAERTNER** (Thyroid & Parathyroid)	THROAT / THYROID & Parathyroid / "Malnutrition & Malassimilation"	**PHOS.**, Calc-f.,p.,-sil., **MERC.**, Phyt., Cupr., Nat-p., Kali-p., Zinc-p., Bary-p./s., Bufo / **BAC.**, **CARC.**, Oscilloc., Strept., Syph., **TUB.** / Berlin Wall, *Blue*, Buddleja, Copper Beach, Goldfish, Moldevite, Pink, Pluto, Sycamore Seed, Turquoise
Circulatory Disorders **PROTEUS** (Thymus Gland)	HEART / HEART & THYMUS Gland / "Brainstorm"	Apis, **AUR.**, Bar.-c.,-m., Bor., Crat., Cupr., Dig., Glon., **IGN.**, Kali-m., Lach., Mag-m., Naja, **NAT-M.**, Stram. / Bac., Bac-ts., Coli., Med., **SYPH.**, Tub. / Adamas, Berlin Wall., Emerald, Frankincense, Hornbeam, *Green*, Pink, Sea-Salt, Silver Birch, Sol.
ALLERGIES **MORGAN-GAERTNER** (Pancreas)	SOLAR PLEXUS / PANCEAS, LIVER & Gallbladder / "Easily offended"	Chel., Hep-s., **KALI-C.** + Nat-m., Lac-h., **LYC.**, Merc., Sang., Sil. + Puls., Staph., Tarax. / **CARC.**, Cytom., Hepatitis, Parat., **TUB.** / Lumbricus, Okou., Red, Rice, Ruby, Sandalwood, *Yellow*
Vaccination Damage **SYCOTIC CO** (Uterus, Ovaries, Prostate, Testes)	SACRAL / GONADS & Spleen / "Irritability"	Card-m., **CHAM.**, Chel., Cina, Equis., Ferr-p., Hydr., Lyc., Mag-m., Merc., Nat-s., Nit-ac., **NUX-V.**, Puls., **RHUS-T.,-V.**, **SEP**, **SIL**, **STANN.**, Tarax., **THUJA** / **AIDS**, **BAC.**, Chlam., Herp-s./,-z., Maland., **MED.**, Pyrog., Scirr., **TUB.**, Vac., Varicella, Vario. / Amethyst, Green, **OAK**, *Orange*, Red Chestnut, Rose Quartz
Basic MINERALS **MORGAN BACH & PURE** (Adrenal Gland, Kidney)	BASE / ADRENAL Glands / "Survival & Congestion"	Alum., Berb., Cadm-s., **CALC-C.,-P.,-F**, Carb-v.,-s, Cean., Con., Dig., Ferr., Graph., Mag-p.,-s, Mang., Nat-c., Petr., Plb., Sars., Sil., Stront-c., **SULPH**, Symph. / Lepro., **PSOR.**, Ringworm, **TUB-BOV.** / Ayahuasca, Clay, Copper Beach, Holly, Jet, Lotus, Lumbricus, Moonstone, Oak, Obsidian, *Red*, Rose Quartz, Sea Holly, Sequoia, Silverfish

Bibliography

Astrology

Damian, Peter. *An Astrological Study of the Bach Flower Remedies.* Neville Spearman Publishers, 1986

Mayo, Jeff. *Astrology – Teach yourself.* Hodder and Stoughton, 1992

Esoteric

Bailey, Alice A. *Esoteric Healing.* NY: Lucis Publishing Company, 1998

Bendit, Lawrence J. and Bendit, Phoebe D. *The Etheric Body of Man.* USA: The Theosophical Publishing House, 1989

Croxon, Paula Byerly. *The Piatkus Dictionary of Mind, Body and Spirit'.* Piatkus Publishers Ltd., 2003

Lady Sabrina. *Celebrating Wiccan Spirituality.* New Page Books, The Career Press, 2003

Aïvanhov, Omraam Mikhaël. *Complete Works of the Second Birth.* France: PROSVETA, 1976

Aïvanhov, Omraam Mikhaël. *Complete Works – Spiritual Alchemy.* France: PROSVETA, 1976

Heindel, Max. *The Rosicrucian Cosmo-Conception.* Rosicrucian Fellowship – First Edition, 1909

Leadbeater, C.W. *Die Chakras.* Freiburg: Herman Bauer Verlag, 1998

Müller, Brigitte. *Energie der 12 Sonnen-Chakra Strahlen.* München: Verlag Peter Erd, 1997

Paulson, Genevieve Lewis. *Kundalini and the Chakras – Practical Manual.* Llewellyn Publications, 2000

Tansley, David V. *Radionics & the Subtle Anatomy of Man.* The C.W. Daniel Company Limited, 1998

Walsch, Neale Donald. *Conversations with God – Book One.* Hodder and Stoughton, 1997

Wauters, Ambika. *Journey of Self Discovery – How to work with the Energies of Chakras and Archetypes.* Judy Piatkus Publishers Ltd., 1996

General

Room, Adrian. *Brewer's Dictionary of Phrases & Fables.* Millennium Edition. Cassell & Co., 2001

Cooper, Primrose. *The Healing Power of Light.* Judy Piatkus Publishers Ltd, 2000

Biedermann, Prof. Dr Hans. *Knaurs Lexikon der Symbole.* Droemersche Verlagsanstalt, 2004

Boericke & Dewey. *The Twelve Tissue Remedies of Schuessler.* B. Jain Publishers PVT Ltd., 1995

Carey, George Washington & Perry, Inez Eudora. *The Zodiac and the Salts of Salvation.* Samuel Weiser Inc., 1996

Clark, Hulda Regehr PhD., N.D. *Heilung ist möglich.* München: Droemersche Verlagsanstalt Th. Knaur Nachf., 1997

Clark, Hulda Regehr PhD., N.D. *The Cure for all Cancers.* USA: New Century Press, 1993

Gittleman, Ann Louise. *Guess what came to Dinner – Parasites and your health.* Avery Publishing Group Inc., 1993

Gray, John. *Men are from Mars, Women are from Venus.* Harper Collins Publisher, 1992

Gray, Robert. *The Colon Health Handbook – New Health Through Colon Rejuvenation.* USA: Robert Gray, 1990

Havard, C.W.H. *Black's Medical Dictionary – 35th Edition.* A & C Black (Publishers) Ltd., 1987

Jensen, Bernard PhD. *The Chemistry of man.* Bernard Jensen, Publisher, 1983

McTaggart, Lynne. *The FIELD – The Quest for the Secret Force of the Universe.* Harper Collins Publishers, 2001

Mandal, Bibhat K., & Mayon-White Richard T. *Lecture Notes on the Infectious Diseases* Fourth Edition. Blackwell Scientific Publications, 1984

Walton, John, Barondess, Jeremiah & Lock, Stephen. *The Oxford Medical Companion.* Oxford University Press, 1994

Shaw, William PhD. *Biological Treatments for Autism and PDD.* USA: Sunflower Publications, 1998

Youngson Dr Robert. *The Royal Society of Medicine Health Encyclopaedia.* The Softback Preview, 2000

Homoeopathy

Agrawal Dr Y.R. *Materia Medica of Glandular Medicines.* Delhi: Vijay Publications, 1992

Agrawal Dr Y.R. *A Treatise on Bowel Nosodes.* Delhi: Vijay Publications, 1995

Fisher, Leslie. *The Clinical Science of Mineral Therapy.* The Maurice Blackmore Research Foundation, 1993

Gaier, Harald C., DHomM., ND, DO, DipAc. *Thorsons Encyclopaedic Dictionary of Homoeopathy.* Harper Collins Publisher 1991

Popp, Prof. Fritz-Albert. *Bericht an Bonn.* VGM Verlag für Ganzheitsmedizin, 1986

Murphy, Robin, N.D. *Homeopathic Medical Repertory.* Hahnemann Academy of North America, 1996

Murphy, Robin, N.D. *Lotus Materia Medica.* Lotus Star Academy, 1995

Saxena, Rajeev Dr. *Phenomenological study of NOSODES.* New Delhi: B. Jain Publisher (P) Ltd., 2002

Squire, Berkeley. *Repertory of Homoeopathic Nosodes and Sarcodes.* New Delhi: B. Jain Publisher (P) Ltd., 2003

Wauters, Ambika. *Homeopathic Colour Remedies.* California: The Crossing Press Freedom, 1999

Weeks, Nora. *The Medical Discoveries of Edward Bach, Physician.* The C. W. Daniel Company Ltd., 1959

Wood, Matthew. *The Magical Staff – The Vitalist Tradition in Western Medicine.* North Atlantic Books, 1992

Iridology

Bamer, Dr Donald R. *Practical Iridology and Sclerology.* Woodland Publishing, 1996

Colton, James & Colton, Sheelagh. *Iridology –Health Analysis & Treatments from the Iris of the Eye.* Element Books Ltd., 1996

Hall, Dorothy. *Iridology – How to discover your own pattern of health and well-being through the eye.* Judy Piatkus Publishers Ltd., 1994

Jensen, Dr Bernard. *Iridology – the Science and Practise in the Healing Arts.* Bernard Jensen, 1982

Jensen, Dr Bernard and Bodeen, Dr Donald V. *Visions of Health – Understanding Iridology.* NY: Avery Publishing Group Inc., 1992

Jensen, Dr Bernard. *What is Iridology? Illustrated.* Bernard Jensen, 1984

Kriege, Theodor. *Fundamental Basis of Irisdiagnosis.* L.N. Fowler & Co. Ltd., 1997

Lindlahr, Henry M.D. *Irisdiagnosis and other diagnostic methods.* Saffron Walden: The C. W. Daniel Company Ltd., 1985

Glossary of Remedies

Abbreviation	Remedy name	Type/Origin
Acon.	Aconite napellus	Monkshood. Wolfsbane.
Adam.	Adamas	White Diamond
Alf.	Alfalfa	California Clover
All-c.	Allium Cepa	Common red onion
Alum.	Alumina	Pure Clay
Ambr.	Ambra grisea	Ambergris – Sea animal
Amethyst	Amethyst	Gemstone
Am-m.	Ammonium Muriaticum	Ammonium chloride
Anac.	Anacardium orientale	Marking Nut
Ant-t.	Antimonium tartaricum	Tartrate of Antimony
Apis	Apis mellifica	Honey-bee poison
Aral.	Aralia racemosa	Spikenard
Arg.	Argentum Metallicum	Silver – Element – Metal
Arg-n.	Argentum nitricum	Silver Nitrate
Arn.	Arnica montana	Leopard's bane.
Ars.	Arsenicum album	Metallic Arsenic
Ars-i.	Arsenicum Iodatum	Iodide of Arsenic
Ash Tree	Ash Tree	Fraxinus Excel.
Aur.	Aurum Metallicum	Metallic Gold
Aur-m.	Aurum Muriaticum	Chloride of Gold
Aven.	Avena sativa	Oat-straw
Ayahuasca	Ayahuasca	Climbing plant
Bar-c.	Baryta carbonica	Carbonate of Baryta
Bar-m.	Baryta muriatica	Chloride of Barium
Bar-p.	Baryta phosphorus	Phosphorus of Barium
Bar-s.	Baryta sulphurica	Sulphur of Barium
Bay leaf	Laurus nobilis	Small Evergreen tree
Bell.	Belladonna	Deadly Nightshade
Bell-p.	Bellis perennis	Daisy
Benz-ac.	Benzoicum acidum	Benzoic Acid
Berb.	Berberis vulgaris	Oregon Grape
Berlin Wall	Berlin Wall	A piece of Berlin Wall
Blue	Blue	Colour
Bor.	Borax veneta	Natrum boricum
Brom.	Bromium	Bromine
Buddleja	Buddleja Davidii	Butterfly bush
Bufo	Bufo rana	Toad poison
Cact.	Cactus grandiflorus	Night blooming Cereus
Cadm-s.	Cadmium sulphuratum	Sulphide of Cadmium
Calc.	Calcarea carbonica	Calcium Carbonate
Calc-f.	Calcarea fluorata	Calcium Fluoride
Calc-i.	Calcarea iodata	Iodide of Lime – Calcium
Calc-p.	Calcarea phosphorica	Calcium Phosphate
Calc-sil.	Calcarea silicata	Silicate of Calcium
Calc-s.	Calcarea sulphurica	Calcium Sulphate
Calen.	Calendula officinalis	Marigold
Cann-i.	Cannabis indica	Hashish
Canth.	Cantharis vesicatoria	Spanish fly
Carb-an.	Carbo animalis	Animal charcoal
Carb-veg.	Carbo vegetabilis	Vegetable charcoal
Carbn-s.	Carboneum sulphuratum	Carbon Sulphur
Card-m.	Carduus marianus	St. Mary's Thistle
Caul.	Caulophyllum thalictroides	Blue Cohosh
Cean.	Ceanothus Americanus	Red root or New Jersey tea
Chalc.	Chalcancite	Crystal

Abbreviation	Remedy name	Type/Origin
Chalice Well	Chalice Well	Glastonbury's Spring Water
Cham.	Chamomilla vulgaris	German Chamomile
Chel.	Chelidonium majus	Greater Celandine
Chin.	China officinalis	Peruvian bark
Cina	Cina maritima	Wormseed
Cinnb.	Cinnabaris	Red Sulphide of Mercury
Clay	Clay	Type of Soil
Cocc.	Cocculus indicus	Indian Cockle
Con.	Conium maculatum	Poison Hemlock
Copper Beach	Copper Beach	Fagus Sylvatica
Cotton	Cotton	Gossypium herbaceum
Crat.	Crataegus oxyacantha	Hawthorn Berries
Crot-h.	Crotalus horridus	Rattlesnake
Cupr.	Cuprum Metallicum	Copper – Element – Metal
Cygn-c.	Cygnus-Cygnus	Whooper Swan
Dig.	Digitalis purpurea	Fox-glove
Dros.	Drosera rotundifolia	Round-leaved Sundew
Echi.	Echinacea angustifolia	Purple Corn-flower
Emerald	Emerald	Gemstone
Equis.	Equisetum hyemale	Horse-tail herb
Ether	Etherum	Well-known anaesthetic
Euph.	Euphrasia officinalis	Eyebright
Ferr.	Ferrum Metallicum	Iron – Element – Metal
Ferr-i.	Ferrum Iodatum	Iodide of Iron
Ferr-m.	Ferrum Muriaticum	Iron chlorine
Ferr-p.	Ferrum Phosphoricum	White phosphate of Iron
Frankincense	Frankincense	Boswellia–Evergreen bush
Fuc.	Fucus vesiculosus	Sea-kelp
Gink.	Ginkgo biloba	Galisburin adiantifolia
Glon.	Glonoinum	Nitro-glycerine
Goldfish	Goldfish	Fish–member of carp family
Graph.	Graphites naturalis	Black lead
Green	Green	Colour
Ham.	Hamanelis virginica	Witch-hazel
Hecla-l.	Hecla lava	Ash from Mount Hecla
Helia.	Helianthus annuus	Sunflower
Hell.	Helleborus niger	Black Hellebore
Hep.	Hepar Sulphuris Calcarea	Calc. Sulph. Hahnemanni
Holly	Holly	Ilex aquifolium
Hornbeam	Hornbeam	Carpinus betulus
HyDr	Hydrastis canadensis	Golden Seal
Hyos.	Hyoscyamus niger	Henbane. Stinking Roger
Hyper.	Hypericum perforatum	St. John's Wort
Ign.	Ignatia	St. Ignatius Bean
Indigo	Indigo	Colour
Iod.	Iodum purum	Iodine the Element
Ip.	Ipecacuanha	Ipec Root
Jet	Jet (Whitby)	Black fossil wood
Kali-br.	Kali bromatum	Bromide of Potassium
Kali-c.	Kali carbonicum	Potassium Carbonate
Kali-chl.	Kali chloricum	Potassium Chlorate
Kali-bi.	Kali Bichromicum	Bichromate of Potash
Kali-i.	Kali Iodatum	Potassium Iodide
Kali-m.	Kali Muriaticum	Chloride of Potassium
Kali-p.	Kali Phosphoricum	Phosphate of Potassium
Kali-s.	Kali Sulphuricum	Potassium Sulphate
Kalm.	Kalmia latifolia	Mountain laurel

Abbreviation	Remedy name	Type/Origin
Lac-ac.	Lactic acidum	Milk acid
Lac-c.	Lac Caninum	Dogs' Milk
Lac-f.	Lac felinum	Cat's milk
Lac-h.	Lac humanum	Human Breast Milk
Lach.	Lachesis muta	Bushmaster snake
Lact.	Lactuca virosa	Opium Lettuce
Lept.	Leptandra virginica	Culver's root – Black root
Lob.	Lobelia inflata	Indian Tobacco or Puke weed
Lotus	Lotus	Nelumbo nucifera
Lyc.	Lycopodium clavatum	Club moss
Lyss.	Lyssinum	Rabies Nosode
Lumbricus	Lumbricus	Earthworm
Luna	Luna	Moon Rays
Mag-c.	Magnesia Carbonica	Magnesia carbonas levis
Mag-m.	Magnesia muriatica	Magnesia Chloride
Mag-p.	Magnesia phosphorica	Phosphate of Magnesia
Mang.	Manganum aceticum	Acetate of Manganese
Merc.	Mercurius solubilis	Mercurius vivus. Metallic Mercury – Quicksilver
Merc-i-f.	Mercurius iodatus flavus	Green Iodide of Mercury
Merc-s.	Mercurius Sulphurica	Mercurius sulphur
Mill.	Millefolium	Yarrow
Mim-h.	Mimosa humilis	Sensitive Plant –Mimosa
Moldevite	Moldevite	Tektite – piece of meteorite
Moonstone	Moonstone	Gem Essence
Naja	Naja tripudians	Cobra venom
Nat-c.	Natrum carbonicum	Sodium carbonate
Nat-i.	Natrum Iodatum	Iodide of Sodium
Nat-m.	Natrum Muriaticum	Salt –common rock salt
Nat-p.	Natrum Phosphoricum	Sodium Phosphate
Nat-s.	Natrum Sulphuricum	Sodium Sulphate
Nit-ac.	Nitricum acidum.	Nitric acid
Nux-m.	Nux moschata	Nutmeg
Nux-v.	Nux Vomica	Poison nut (Strychnos)
Oak	Oak	Quercus robur
Obsidian	Obsidian	Gemstone
Okou.	OkoubakaAubrevillei	Santalaceae
Op.	Opium	Poppy
Orange	Orange	Colour
Oxyg.	Oxygenium	Oxygen
Passi.	Passiflora incarnata	Passion Flower
Petros.	Petroselinum sativum	Parsley
Ph-ac.	Phosphoricum acidum	Phosphoric acid
Phos.	Phosphorus	Phosphorus the Element
Phyt.	Phytolacca decandra	Poke-root – Poke weed
Pic-ac.	Picricum acidum	Picric Acid
Pink	Pink	Colour
Plan.	Plantago major	Plantain / Ribwort
Plat.	Platina	Platinum Metallicum
Podo.	Podophyllum peltatum	MayApple/AmericanMandrake
Plb.	Plumbum Metallicum	Lead the Element – Metal
Plut.	Plutonium	Radioactive metallic element
Puls.	Pulsatilla nigricans	Wind flower – Pasque flower
Purple	Purple	Colour
Rainbow	Rainbow	Rainbow (Spectrum)
Red Chestnut	Chestnut Red	Castanea tree
Rhodocrosite	Rhodocrosite	Gem Essence

Abbreviation	Remedy name	Type/Origin
Rice	Rice – Brown organic	Rice
Rose Quartz	Rose Quartz	Gem Essence
Rhus-t.	Rhus toxicodendron	Poison Ivy
Ruby	Ruby	Gem Essence
Sabal.	Sabal serrulata	Saw Palmetto
Salix Fragilis	Salix Fragilis	Crack Willow tree
Sandalwood	Sandalwood – white	Santalum album
Sang.	Sanguinaria canadensis	Blood-root
Sars.	Sarsaparilla officinalis	Wild Liquorice
Sea Holly	Sea Holly	Eryngium maritimum
Sea-Salt	Sea Salt (Winchelsea)	Evaporated Seawater
Sec.	Secale cornutum	Ergot of Rye
Sep.	Sepia succus	Cuttle Fish Ink
Sequoia	Sequoia	Giant Redwood tree
Scorp.	Scorpio Europaeus	Scorpion
Sil.	Silicea terra	Pure Flint
Silver Birch	Silver Birch	Betula pendula
Silverfish	Silverfish	Insect
Skook.	Skookum chuck aqua.	Medicinal lake – USA
Sol.	Sol. Britannicus	Sunlight – Britannia
Solid.	Solidago virgaurea	Golden-rod
Spectrolite	Spectrolite	Type of Feldspar
Spig-m.	Spigelia marylandica	Worm-grass
Spon.	Spongia tosta	Roasted Sponge
Stann.	Stannum Metallicum	Tin the Element – Metal
Staph.	Staphysagria	Delphinium
Stonehenge	Stonehenge	Sacred Druid site in England
Stram.	Stramonium	Jimson weed – Thornapple
Stront-c.	Strontium carbonicum	Carbonate of Strontium
Sul-ac.	Sulphuricum acidum	Sulphuric acid
Sulph.	Sulphur	Sulphur – Brimstone
Sycamore Seed	Sycamore Seed	Two-winged seed from Sycamore tree
Symph.	Symphytum officinale	Comfrey – healing herb
Tarax.	Taraxacum officinale	Dandelion
Tarent.	Tarentula hispanica	Spanish Tarantula – Spider
Teucr.	Teucrium marum verum	Cat-thyme
Thios.	Thiosinamium	Mustard Seed Oil
Thuj.	Thuja occidentalis	Arbor Vitae – Coniferae
Tiger-eye	Tiger-eye	Gem Essence
Turquoise	Turquoise	Gem Essence and Colour
Urt-u.	Urtica urens	Stinging nettle
Valer.	Valeriana officinalis	Valerian
Verat.	Veratrum album	White Hellebore
Verat-v.	Veratrum viride	American White Hellebore
Verb.	Verbascum thapsus	Mullein Oil
Yellow	Yellow	Colour
Zinc.	Zincum metallicum	Zinc the Element – Metal
Zinc-p.	Zincum phosphoricum	Phosphorus of Zinc

Table of Nosodes and Bowel Nosodes

Aids	Aids Nosode	Nosode
Ba-sv (or Bac no.7)	Bacillus asiaticus –	Bacillus No. 7 Paterson
Ba-tn (or Bac no.10)	Bacillus number 10	Bacillus No. 10 Paterson
Bac.	Bacillinum	Tubercular Nosode
Bac-ts.	Bacillinum Testium	Tubercular Testicle-human
Cand-a.	Candida albicans	Fungi
Carc.	Carcinosin	Cancer Nosode
Chlam-t.	Chlamydia trachomatis	Type of parasite
Coli. (Coli-bac.)	Coli-bacillinum	Escherichia coli – serum
Cytom.	Cytomegalovirus	Virus
Dys-co.	Dysentery co.	Bacillus Dysenteriae /Bach
Gaert.	Gaertner (Bacillus)	Salmonella enteridis /Bach
Hepatitis (various)	Hepatitis A/B	Virus
Herp-s.	Herpes simplex	Virus
Herp-z.	Herpes zoster	Virus
Lepro.	Leprominium	Leprosy Nosode
Maland.	Malandrinum	Grease of horses
Med.	Medorrhinum	Gonorrhoea Nosode
Morg.	Morgan pure	Bacillus Morgan pure Paterson
Morg-g.	Morgan Gaertner	Bacillus Morgan Gaertner Paterson
Oscilloc. or Anas Barb.	Oscillococcinum	Bacteria
Parat.	Paratyphoidinum	Bacteria
Prot.	Proteus	Bacillus Proteus / Bach (mirabilis reltgeri)
Psor.	Psorinum	Scabies Nosode
Pyrog.	Pyrogen	Rotten meat pus
Ringworm	Ringworm – various fungi Tinea-barbea = beard Tinea-capitis= on scalp Tinea-pedis=athlete's foot	Fungi – TINEA
Scirr.	Scirrhinum	Scirrhus Cancer
Syc-co.	Sycotic-co.	Streptococcus faecalis Paterson
Staphycoc.	Staphylococcinum	Bacteria Staphylococcus
Strept.	Streptococcinum	Bacteria Streptococcus
Syph.	Syphilinum / Lueticum	Bacteria/Syphilitic Nosode
Tub-b.	Tuberculinum Bovinum	Tuberculosis Bacillus/Kent
Tub-k.	Tuberculinum Koch	Tuberculosis Nosode
Vac.	Vaccininum	Vaccine Nosode
Varicella	Varicella	Chickenpox Nosode
Vario.	Variolinum	Small-pox Nosode

Table of Sarcodes

A.C.T.H.	Adrenocorticotrophic	Hormone
Adren.	Adrenalinum	Extract of Adrenal glands
Calcitonin	Calcitonin or Thyroid-calcitonin	Hormone from the Thyroid Gland
Chol.	Cholesterinum	Cholesterine – Gallstones
Corp-l.	Corpus Luteum	Flaveinum Lutenum
Foll.	Folliculinum	Ovarian Follicle
Hypoth.	Hypothalamus	Extract
Insulin	Insulinum	Pancreatic Insulin
Kidney	Kidney	Kidney
Lac-hum.	Lac Humanum	Human Breast Milk
Mamm.	Glandular Mamma	Breast tissue
Melant.	Melatonin	Pineal Gland Hormone
Orch.	Orchitinum	Testicular extract
Ov.	Ovininum – Oophorinum	Ovary Gland
Pancreat.	Pancreatinum & Pancreas	Extract
Parath.	Parathyroid Gland	Extract
Pep.	Pepsinum	Enzyme
Pineal	Pineal Gland	Extract
Pitu-gl. & Pituin.	Pituitary Gland	Extract
Plac.	Placenta Humana	Human Placenta
Prost.	Prostate Gland	Extract
Secret.	Secretinum	Secretin from Duodenum
Serot.	Serotoninum	Hormone - vasoconstrictor
Splen.	Splenum	Spleen
Thym-gl.	Thymus Gland	Extract
Thyr.	Thyroid Gland	Extract
Thyri.	Thyroiodinum	Iodine and Thyroid extract
Uter.	Uterus	Extract

Index

A

161

P

T